The PATH of SCIENCE

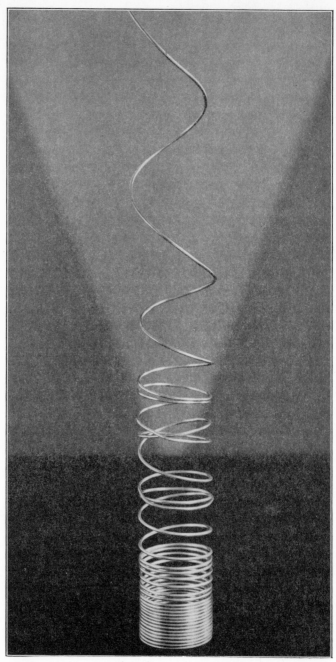

The Helix of History

The PATH of SCIENCE

By

C. E. KENNETH MEES, D.Sc., F.R.S.

Vice President in charge of Research
Eastman Kodak Company
Rochester, New York

with the co-operation of

JOHN R. BAKER, M.A., D.Phil., D.Sc.

Lecturer in Zoology in the
University of Oxford, England

New York: JOHN WILEY & SONS, Inc.

London: CHAPMAN & HALL, Limited

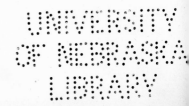

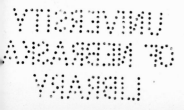

"The present should retain its true proportion—a moment between an infinite past and a hurrying future."

Time and Chance, JOAN EVANS
London, 1943

PREFACE

In 1943 I was invited to accept the Hitchcock professorship at the University of California. The Hitchcock professor is expected to give a course of public lectures, and the subject selected was the development of science and its relation to the history of society. These lectures have been expanded into this book with the purpose of presenting the development of modern science against the background of history.

There is not room for a complete history of science in a book of this type, but Chapters V, VI, and VII are intended to give an account of the growth of ideas in the three major sciences so that the reader can understand how the ideas of modern science have developed.

My thanks are due to many friends for criticism and assistance and especially to Dr. John R. Baker, who wrote Chapter VII, *The Growth of Biological Ideas,* and whose criticism of the whole manuscript as it progressed has been most valuable.

Although the book is largely historical, Dr. Baker and I are not professional historians of science. Dr. Baker is an investigator in pure science, and I am a director of industrial scientific research. It is hoped that our active participation in the advance of science and technology has given us a viewpoint that compensates for the lack of historical training.

C. E. K. MEES

Rochester, N. Y.
1946

CONTENTS

Résumé of the ideas of science and the methods by which these ideas have been evolved.   A brief account of science intended to give a picture of the whole to an educated man.

The present organization for scientific research and the developments in that organization likely to occur in the near future.

Organization of industrial scientific research and the application of science to industry.

The relation of science to society and the proposals made for the application of science to the study of sociology and politics.   Résumé of the path of science as a whole in its relation to human society.

Chapter I

THE INTERPRETATION OF HISTORY

Ever since men have written down their thoughts for the benefit of their successors, they have tried to peer into the future to form some idea of the events to come. For this purpose, they have relied upon auguries and upon observations of the stars; but the only method that is now generally accepted is based on consideration of the past and expectation that the future will follow the trends of the past, especially the recent past.

Sometimes the conditions of human life continue unchanged for long periods. Excavation of the cities of the past, as well as their recorded history, shows us that often life continued in those cities for generation after generation with little change in the way of living and even little change in the material things—the tools and weapons used by the people. During such periods of stability, the records show a general belief that the stability would continue, that human civilization is essentially a static system. As the Preacher writes, "The thing that hath been, it is that which shall be; and that which is done is that which shall be done: and there is no new thing under the sun." *

In attempting to look into the future by the use of our records of the past, we are trying to discern in history some general principles that we may expect to govern the order of events. F. A. von Hayek considers it a contradiction in terms to demand that history should become a theoretical science and believes that the demand arises from the study of the social sciences by those trained in the natural sciences who

* *Ecclesiastes* I:9.

1

attempt to create a new science of society to satisfy their own ideals. Von Hayek considers that the events of history are "unique" and that "the creation and dissolution of the Roman Empire or the Crusades, the French Revolution or the Growth of Modern Industry are unique complexes of events which have helped to contribute the particular circumstances in which we live and whose explanation is therefore of great interest." *

However, while we may accept the view that the facts of human history are unordered in detail, it is not impossible that taken on a broad scale they may show some order. There is nothing obviously false in assuming that human history passes through cycles during which there is a change in some factor in a definite direction. It would be possible, for instance, for the length of human life to vary either progressively or periodically as time continued. As far as the author knows, there is no evidence for such a phenomenon; but if the facts suggested it, there is no fundamental reason for rejecting it. H. G. Wells, indeed, holds that we are justified in considering history as a whole to be a science.† He says, "History is no exception amongst the sciences; as the gaps fill in, the outline simplifies; as the outlook broadens, the clustering multitude of details dissolve into general laws." The nature of these laws is evidently of the first importance, since upon them will depend the future that we may expect and, therefore, any action that we may take to modify that future. No pattern that we can detect in history can possibly foretell the future in detail; the past contains no maps of the things to come. Nevertheless, history does fall into patterns "as the outlook broadens," and these patterns may be valuable for our guidance.

The views that men have held of the patterns of history have had the greatest influence upon the whole thought of

* F. A. von Hayek, "Scientism and the Study of Society, II," *Economica*, N.S., **10**, 34 (1943).

† H. G. Wells, Introduction to *The Outline of History*, London, George Newnes, Ltd., 1920.

man. They have, indeed, been among those "ideas" that have dominated the imagination and directed the actions of mankind. After the destruction of the ancient world that preceded the classical period—the world of Babylonia and Egypt, Crete and the Hittite Empire, the world that was at its height of prosperity in the fifteenth century before Christ— there was a great period of darkness, in which the Hellenes who had invaded western Asia Minor and Greece were slowly advancing from their barbarian culture, much apparently as the Saxons advanced slowly after they had destroyed the Roman culture that they had found in Britain. In both cases, the destruction of the old culture was extraordinarily complete. In England, the very ditches had been abandoned, so that when the cultivation of the fields was resumed, new lines of drainage had to be established, a change that requires centuries. In Greece, the art of writing appears to have been lost, and the earliest writers of the reviving civilization borrowed their alphabet from Semitic sources. This, however, had its advantages. The Greeks started with a "clean slate." As Bacon reminds us, they had no knowledge of antiquity, and it is interesting to reflect that the classical Greeks spent no time learning foreign languages. They were, in fact, almost the only people of antiquity who did not devote themselves to that occupation, which today is considered such a necessary discipline. The Babylonian youth had to learn Sumerian, in which his classical books were written, and the Roman regarded a knowledge of Greek as essential. But the Greeks had no venerated classics, no holy books, no dead languages to master, no authorities to check their free speculation.

Since the Greeks had no knowledge of any long period of history, they had little material from which to get an idea of a pattern in history. They recognized that man had progressed from a state of barbarism, and they ascribed his progress to the invention and assistance of the gods. At the same time, they held to the old legend of a past golden age, a period of well-being and innocence from which man had fallen, and thus they developed a theory of the rise and fall of culture and civilization. In Plato's writings we find the view expressed that the world had been created as a perfect world, but that it was not immortal and had in it the seeds of decay, so that in time it would degenerate completely and would be destroyed if the Creator did not intervene and start the cycle again. The first stage of such a cycle would be the golden age of legend, and the period in which the Greeks found themselves they considered to be one of gradual decay and degeneration. This view was in accordance with the whole attitude of the Greeks toward life, an attitude of skepticism and of pessimism. To a Greek philosopher, man was a small figure in a great and turbulent universe, struggling against the will of the pitiless gods who held his fate in their hands and played with it for amusement; so that finally the lesson was laid down that a man must do all that he can and that then, having failed, he must be prepared to suffer all that he can suffer. This philosophy was expressed not only by the philosophers themselves but it was stated even more clearly by the tragic poets who had so great an influence on Greek thought and who have retained that influence in the thought of men to this day.

Plato's theory of world cycles became the orthodox theory of history among the Greeks and passed from them to the Romans. According to some of the followers of Pythagoras, each cycle repeated to the minutest particular the course and events of the preceding cycle. This theory was adopted by the Stoics and is referred to by Marcus Aurelius in his *Meditations*. He says that the "rational soul" contemplates the grand revolutions of nature and the destruction and renewal of the universe. So uniform is the course of history that a man of forty years may know all the past and all the future.

There was a moment in Greek history when the Greek scholars stood on the edge of the discovery of the method of experimental science. For that moment they saw the possibility of a different idea of history, and the Epicureans rejected the doctrine of a golden age and a subsequent degeneration and believed instead that the earliest condition of men had been that of animals and that civilization had been developed by the exercise of human intelligence. Expression of this school is found in the work of Lucretius, the Roman poet who restated the philosophical ideas of Epicurus in Latin hexameters. But the pessimism of the Greeks was too fundamental for this view to be maintained, and Lucretius himself expresses his skepticism of the value of civilization. When Prometheus stole the fire from heaven and Icarus adopted wings, they paid for their daring the penalty that they owed to the gods whom they had challenged. The Greeks were resigned, in fact, to a fixed order of the universe, and any idea of progress toward perfection would have been a violation of that fixed order.

The organization of Europe under the Romans did nothing to make men feel that a definite progress in the conditions of mankind was possible. Those conditions, indeed, were bad, at best. The economic foundation of the Roman Empire was unsound. Its government was a totalitarian tyranny. It is not without significance that the historical doctrines of German National Socialism are akin to those of Marcus Aurelius.

With the rise of Christianity, an entirely new idea of human history was introduced—the idea that life on earth was on the verge of ceasing. For St. Augustine, as for any believer of that time, the course of history would be satisfactorily complete if the world came to an end in his own lifetime. The Christian church had started as a group of disciples waiting for the return of their leader, and for the early church the orthodox theory was that the Second Coming might be expected at any time. Moreover, the basis of the Christian religion was the idea of the individual's fall from grace and his redemption from sin by the sacrifice of the god. History, then, was the history of a degenerate world, some of which might finally be redeemed and, with that redemption, obliterated by absorption into the godhead.

The great change in these ideas came at the beginning of the seventeenth century and was expressed most clearly in the work of Francis Bacon. The part that Bacon played in the growth of science will be discussed later. We are at present concerned only with the effect that he produced upon the thought of his time. Bacon was not a scientist or an experimenter; he was a theorist and planner. He laid down an ambitious program for a great renovation of knowledge based upon his view that the secrets of nature could be determined by experiment and that the value of scientific knowledge lay in its utility. Thus the proper end of human knowledge was the amelioration of the conditions of human life. For this purpose Bacon saw that organized scientific research—the study of the learning of the past and the development of new learning by direct observation and experiment—must result in the most important advances. He pointed out that three great inventions unknown to the ancients—printing, gunpowder, and the compass—"have changed the appearance and state of the whole world; first in literature, then in warfare, and lastly in navigation; and innumerable changes have been thence derived, so that no empire, sect, or star appears to have exercised a greater power or influence on human affairs than these mechanical discoveries." *

With Bacon and with the increase in scientific discovery that followed, the idea of progress became the dominant theory of history. This was supported by the philosophy of René Descartes, who insisted on the invariability of the laws of nature and the supremacy of reason, which, carried to a logical conclusion, excluded the doctrine of providence, the basic belief of the Christian philosophers. The development of the idea of progress through the seventeenth and eighteenth centuries is of interest primarily to a student of philosophy.†
It was embodied in Immanuel Kant's philosophy and in the

---

* Francis Bacon, *Novum Organum*, 129.

† For an excellent discussion of the subject, see J. B. Bury, *The Idea of Progress*, New York, The Macmillan Co., 1932.

positivism of Auguste Comte. It was perhaps a result of Comte's work that the idea of progress became so completely accepted by the people of the nineteenth century, and it is, of course, the basis of Herbert Spencer's philosophy, embodied in his *First Principles,* published in 1862. Belief in progress was greatly reinforced by the rapid development of science and technology and by the manifest improvement in the conditions of life.

Nevertheless, the cyclic theory of history, held by the Greeks, has not been abandoned in modern times. The theories of Plato and Polybius, that the history of states must repeat itself, were worked out in detail by Vico in the eighteenth century and used as a fundamental theory of history by Brooks Adams in his *Law of Civilization and Decay.* Adams bases his interpretation on psychology, seeing in fear and greed the two great motives for human action. These two motives, he thought, alternate through the course of history, so that we have first a stage in which fear predominates and civilization is organized on a military and imaginative basis. In this stage, there is an accumulation of wealth, and society is centralized. This centralized society then transfers its central motive from fear and the military state to greed and the economic state. The productive power of this state collapses as a result of the greed of the individuals in a capitalistic society, and the military phase of expansion recurs.

Brooks Adams takes a deeply pessimistic view of human history and, indeed, of human nature. According to him, men have been almost invariably scoundrels inspired by fear or by greed. Such a view of the motives that have moved men in the past and of the characters of those who could be moved almost entirely by such motives is sufficient to refute the entire argument. In the absence of any specific information to the contrary, the best assumption as to the nature of men in the past is that it was the same as that of men in the present. Nevertheless, it is true that nations pass through successive stages of integration and disintegration. States have been built up by conquest and assimilation, and then, with the growth of wealth and leisure, they have been the prey of external aggressors. The aggressors have flourished and have in turn relapsed into weakness and perished. Thus the history of individual nations shows a cyclic rhythm.

Another cyclic theory of history has been developed by Oswald Spengler in his famous book, *The Decline of the West*. Spengler presents history as a succession of cultures, each of which follows a definite course of development through a sequence of phases. He holds that each culture has its own peculiarities but that the course of development through the phases is the same for all. Thus each culture has its beginning, its development based essentially on rural life. It then blossoms into full strength, with the urban population taking control of the thought of the nation until, finally, there comes a decay, particularly of religion and of inward life, and a collapse of the culture as a whole. A necessary part of Spengler's argument is that the same phases are distinguishable in all cultures. He treats the Renaissance as a revolt against the Gothic, the exhaustion of the early phase of modern culture. Similar revolts occurred in Egypt at the close of the Old Kingdom with the development of the feudal system and in Greece at the close of the archaic period, though, surely, the corresponding period in Greek culture should be that at which the Hellenistic displaced the Hellenic. Spengler carries these analogies to the individuals of the phases. He considers Napoleon a parallel to Alexander.

An excellent analysis of Spengler's work has been made by Collingwood, who points out that Spengler carries this theory to an extreme; every phase and every detail reappears in each cycle.[*] Since obviously this is not true of history, the cycles cannot be identical. Rather, they must be homologous —in each cycle the events and personalities must correspond structurally to events and personalities of the past. The task of the historian is, therefore, parallel to that of the comparative anatomist; he must depict the correspondence of the

[*] R. G. Collingwood, "Oswald Spengler and the Theory of Historical Cycles," *Antiquity*, **I**, 311 (1927).

events in two cycles while realizing their differentiation arising from the differences between the cycles. It is useless
merely to mention likenesses in history—to compare Alexander with Caesar or Buddha with Christ. Nevertheless,
these likenesses must be recognized at the same time that
their differences are realized.

Collingwood compares Spengler's cyclic theory with the
doctrines of Plato, Polybius, and Vico, and points out that
Spengler apparently did not know of the work of Sir Flinders
Petrie, which is discussed later. Probably the popularity of
Spengler's book arises from his claim to foretell the future.
According to Spengler, the present era is that of the collapse
of a civilization—a plutocracy disguised by demagogism and
now called "democracy"—corresponding to that of the second
century B.C. in Rome, when the Roman republic was col-
lapsing and the civilization of the ancient world as a whole
was moving toward the tyranny of the Roman Empire and
the darkness that followed it. This idea of Spengler's seems
to lie at the root of much of the totalitarian philosophy. But
Spengler's claim to foretell the future is, as Collingwood
points out, baseless. Even if the general pattern is repeated
in cycles, there is no evidence that those cycles resemble
each other closely enough or are sufficiently uniform in length
or intensity to enable us to predict anything except that there
will continue to be cycles.

The tremendous events of the last ten years, during which
some of the most active and capable nations have challenged
the ideals on which western civilization was founded and
plunged into world-wide war to enforce their challenge, have
produced doubts in the minds of many thinkers as to the
validity of the idea of progress. Some years ago, Mr. Philip
Cabot wrote to a friend:

> The period covered by my father's life, and most of my
> own, was one in which wise men in Western Europe and
> in America looked forward to the future with confidence
> and hope. Of course, their world was menaced by the
> dangers which have always distressed mankind—war, pesti-

lence and famine. But to these the race has become inured, and the hope of this period appeared to be based on reasonable foresight. Their troubles were mostly in the present; their future seemed remarkably secure.

Now the outlook has changed. We still have our present troubles, and to them has been added grave anxiety about the future, an anxiety which is most marked among thoughtful men. For there is reason to doubt whether we shall be able to hand on to our children unimpaired the great social structure which we received from our forefathers.

At the time that Cabot wrote this, he was not thinking directly of the great threat that was developing in Central Europe and that in 1939 broke on the world in a tempest of fire and steel. Instead, as he said in his commencement address to Juniata College on June 1, 1936,* he felt that the dangers that threaten us are internal and arise from the loss of the fundamental agreements upon which the life of our society is based. Social disintegration appeared to him to be foreshadowed in the weakening of family life, the breakdown of social conventions, and especially the decay of religion. These changes arise from the fluidity and increase of wealth and from the great mobility of the population, so that scarcely any families live in the old homestead and few live many years in the same place. People no longer feel that they belong to a definite group, and without such a feeling societies are unlikely to persist.

It is by no means the first time in the history of the world that rapid changes have occurred, both in relation to the material control that man has over his environment and also in relation to the economic and social structure of society. Frequently these changes, accompanied by great mass movements of peoples, have resulted in the destruction of cities and the erection of new empires on the ashes of the old. Between the fourteenth and the twelfth centuries B.C., such a great change occurred and it resulted in the destruction of the oldest stable empires of which we have any record. The

* Philip Cabot, *Addresses 1935–1941*, Cambridge, Mass., 1942.

origin of that change we do not know. It was quite possibly the culmination of climatic changes occurring in the great plains of Eastern Europe and Western Asia. In the course of it, Crete lost her control of the northern Mediterranean and finally vanished from the list of the empires. The Achaean Greek civilization that Crete had founded disappeared in its turn. The Hittite Empire, attacked in the north, pressed through to the south, came into conflict with the new power of Assyria, and was destroyed. Assyria conquered Babylonia and expanded its new empire, which was eventually to overrun Egypt itself.

In the fifth century A.D., a similar rapid change in the organization of world power and, consequently, in the economic and social life of the civilized world took place. The Gothic invasion of Italy after the division of the empire between Rome and Constantinople terminated the domination of the western world by Rome.

In the fifteenth century, again, centralized monarchies took the place of the feudal system, and that system that had ruled the world for a thousand years deliquesced and changed before the eyes of men. And then Northern Europe largely abandoned its traditional religion and established a new church, carrying with it altogether new and different social relations.

But the progress made in the material aspects of civilization in the three hundred years that have elapsed since the birth of Newton is as great as that made from the neolithic period to the time of his birth. A man of Newton's day who left London or Paris and by some Time Machine found himself in ancient Rome, Athens, or Thebes would have missed few of the conveniences and amenities of life to which he had been accustomed. In some respects, indeed, he might have found himself better off. The water supply and the drainage system of ancient Rome were better than those of Elizabethan London. The buildings of Thebes or Athens or Rome were greatly superior to those of London or Paris in the seventeenth century. The mind of man, the intellectual atmosphere, was much the same. The absence of Christianity and especially the extent of slavery would make the social world rather different to our voyager, but for his bodily comfort he would find that he had lost little in returning to the ancient world. But if the man of today should go back to the world in which Newton was born, he might not find himself mentally in a remote world, but physically he would be astonished and shocked. The clothing would strike him as primitive; the houses, as crude and uncomfortable. Few would care to live in Wolsey's palace at Hampton Court, and Wolsey was a man who loved luxury. The sights and the smells, the dirt and the vermin of the cities of that time would be most offensive to him. The inconveniences of travel, the unpaved streets, the absence of sanitation, and the appalling disease would make him realize how great a change has come over the world. He would soon, of course, become accustomed to the conditions, just as men today become accustomed to primitive conditions when they encounter them. But how inconvenient to be without matches, without any satisfactory water system, and, for those who are inveterate readers, to have a very limited supply of books and no satisfactory system of artificial light!

These comforts and conveniences, which are today normally taken for granted, have been achieved by the work of the technologists and scientists of the last three hundred years. Moreover, even the industrial revolution of the nineteenth century probably produced less change in the life of man than has occurred during the first third of the twentieth century. Many writers on sociology have commented on the recent changes in social conditions and in human relations as being psychological and sociological phenomena; and among these are a number of the most distinguished philosophers and thinkers of the present time. A. N. Whitehead, discussing the present as a turning point in the sociological conceptions of western civilization, concludes that throughout the whole of the western world "something has come to an end."

In Russia there has been a revolution, because something has come to an end. In Asia Minor the Turks are recreating novel forms of social life, because something has come to an end. In the larger nations of Western Europe, Italy, Spain, France, Germany, England, there is a turmoil of reconstruction, because something has come to an end.*

But men do not look back when they come to the parting of the ways; they look forward. And the cause of these "revolutions," these "ferments," these "turmoils" is applied science and the promise that men can see in it. C. A. Beard in his introduction to Bury's *Idea of Progress* (*loc. cit.,* page 6) points out that the basis of modern civilization is technology, which indicates the methods by which the conquest of nature can be effected. Technology involves not only the existing machines and processes but still more a philosophy and a method linked, as it were, to the methods and spirit of science. Moreover, technology is world-wide and universal, available to all nations and affecting all classes. Thus technology is at once the source and the justification for the idea of progress. Mankind has not merely advanced from primitive culture; it has developed a working method for a continuation of that advance. There is no reason to believe that the present civilization will run its cycle and relapse into barbarism; there are no limits to the possibilities of scientific discovery and its application to the wants of man. The solution of a scientific problem does not close a chapter; it opens new problems. Moreover, advances in one field of science make possible advances in another. The solution of a physical problem throws light upon chemistry and that, in its turn, on physiology or on medicine. Until man has no more curiosity and no more wants, his quest for knowledge will persist and the application of that knowledge will continue.

What distinguishes the present change in sociological con-

* A. N. Whitehead, "The Study of the Past—Its Uses and Its Dangers," *Harvard Business Review,* **XI,** No. 4, 436 (1933).

ditions from those that have gone before is the *rate* at which the change is occurring. Earlier changes in the social structure, such as those that occurred at the end of the Roman Empire, were extremely slow in comparison with the changes that we have seen in our own lifetimes. At the present time, the rate of change is greater than any in the previous experience of man, and it appears to be still accelerating. The rate is, indeed, so great that it is often said that the world is passing through a social revolution. On this point, one may agree with Cabot that the word "revolution" is too strong. Revolution suggests an explosion, and such an explosion may occur; indeed, the German and Japanese attacks might be considered explosions. But apart from these aggressive actions, which are not necessarily due to the social changes, what is occurring is not social revolution but social evolution at a very rapid pace.

An important contribution to the study of the situation was made by the late Lord Stamp in his book *The Science of Social Adjustment,* the first chapter of which is entitled "The Impact of Science upon Society." * Stamp points out that the specific phenomenon that we have to investigate is what occurs at the point of impact, where the new discoveries and inventions affect our social life, and here the rate of change is of primary importance. In his book he discusses as an economist such matters as the obsolescence of machinery, the displacement of labor, the changes in industry and in the population.

Many of the most important changes produced by science are not generally recognized as such. Everybody realizes that the introduction of the railroad train, the automobile, and the airplane have changed social conditions; but by far the most important factors in the changes that are occurring in society arise from the prolongation of human life. Not a generation ago, life expectation at birth was forty years; today it is sixty. This produces a change in the distribution

* Sir Josiah Stamp, *The Science of Social Adjustment,* London, Macmillan and Co., 1937.

of age among the population—a decrease in the percentage of children and an increase in the numbers of the older—that must have a profound effect upon the organization of society. The problems of India that arise from its political situation, grave as those are, are by no means the most important for the future of the country. As A. V. Hill has pointed out in his report on his visit to India on behalf of the Royal Society, the great problem in India is the extraordinarily rapid increase in the population owing to the improvement in medical and sanitary conditions, far behind those of the western world as they still are. The society of India, with its many complications of custom and religion, was adapted to a large birth rate and an appalling death rate. Even a slight reduction in the death rate has been sufficient to upset the balance.

The growth of science, which made it possible to conceive the idea of progress and which is the source of many improvements in the conditions of human life, has become so rapid that the changes that it produces threaten the very foundations of society. Today we have to face the necessity for a complete re-orientation of our attitude toward social conditions. We can no longer expect the organization of society to remain stable. We must expect it to be changing continually, and we must plan our political and economic control not to perpetuate any existing state of affairs but to meet the changes that will come in such a way that they will give us the maximum benefit and the minimum distress.

In this book we shall discuss the structure of society from the historical point of view, especially its relation to the development of scientific knowledge and the methods that have been and can be used for the production of scientific knowledge.

While the relation between the progress of scientific discovery and the structure of society is of the utmost interest and importance to those who desire to understand it or, still more, to control the changes that are occurring, there is a cleavage between those who follow the discipline of history and of the humanities and those who are eagerly pursuing the quest for scientific knowledge. Humanistic learning is the learning of the ancients; it is a study of the accumulated thought of mankind so far as it has been transmitted to us. Scientific knowledge, on the other hand, is a development arising from the observation of facts and their classification into patterns. The separation of these two types of learning has always been unfortunate; at present it is serious, and it may, indeed, be disastrous. As Sarton says, "The most ominous conflict of our time is the difference of opinion, of outlook, between men of letters, historians, philosophers, the so-called humanists, on the one side, and scientists on the other." * The administrators and organizers of society have been trained chiefly in the humanities and are largely ignorant not only of the facts of science but of the scientific method. The scientists, on the other hand, are absorbed in their own problems and too often have little time to spare for the study of history, even the history of science. It is essential that a reconciliation between the two branches of learning should be effected and that the present dichotomy of our cultural and educational systems should be resolved. The humanists must understand what the scientists have done in the past, are doing now, and may do in the future; while the scientists must see their work in the light of history and in relation to the effects that its application to social conditions will produce.

Now let us turn to the pageant of history and endeavor to see some design in its structure that may reconcile in one general pattern the different conceptions of history that we have discussed.

* George Sarton, *The History of Science and the New Humanism,* p. 54, Cambridge, Harvard University Press, 1937. All quotations from this author are reprinted by permission of the publishers.

Chapter II

THE HELIX OF HISTORY

History involves the study of human progress. The record of that progress is to be found on the earth itself—a fragmentary record of graves and building stones, of broken tools and potsherds—which can be interpreted to give the story of the ascent of man. But the greater part of history as it is written by historians is the history of written documents. Indeed, many historians maintain that only written documents can supply trustworthy history and that evidence from other sources is not really history but should be dealt with as a separate science, the science of archaeology. The result is that the historian often fails to give the reader a perspective of human history as a whole because he finds it necessary to devote practically all his space to discussions of the written evidence and the rewording of the writings of his predecessors. As Gordon Childe points out in his essay on the writing of history, this is particularly unfortunate if we are endeavoring to follow the development of science and technology through the ages.* Even those scientific discoveries which are necessarily committed to writing—mathematical calculations and formulae, for instance—have generally been neglected by students who, as Childe says, "were by training inclined to prefer historical and mythological literature and were, in any case, hardly competent to appreciate the true inwardness of the problems the ancient scribes were trying to overcome."

Most of our information on the technology of the ancients is necessarily derived from the material objects discovered by

* Gordon Childe, "The History of Civilization," *Antiquity*, **XV**, 1 (1941).

excavation, and only too often that information is fragmentary and obviously insufficient. The known instrumental
equipment of the Egyptians seems scarcely sufficient for the
great engineering works which they undertook. Was Galileo
or his immediate predecessor really the first to combine two
lenses to make a telescope? While we should certainly not
accept the existence of such instruments in much earlier
times without adequate evidence, we should as certainly not
regard their existence as impossible.

Again, in the absence of definite records, historians tend
to overrate the isolation of countries and cultures in early
times. It is true that in the early part of a cycle of culture, as
in Greece in the eighth century B.C., contact with other countries was largely lost. Six hundred years earlier, however,
communications between Egypt, Babylonia, and Asia Minor
were so good that there was something approximating a postal
service, and because of its convenience correspondents in all
these countries used a common language—Babylonian written
in the cuneiform script. The visit of a Pharaoh of the Old
Kingdom to Crete, imagined by Miss Grant in her novel,
while unlikely, is certainly not impossible.*

To get a true view of the pattern of history, it is necessary
to broaden our outlook as much as possible and to cover not
only the whole of recorded history but also the prehistory of
the archaeologist. As Childe says: "For the prehistorian, the
colonization of the Mediterranean basin by the Phoenicians
and the Greeks is but the continuation of the Minoans' pioneering efforts. To the historian, the empires of Assyria,
Babylon, Persia, and Macedon must appear fulfillments of
the ambitions of Sargon of Agade, Ur-Nammu, and Ham-
murabi."

When we attempt to contemplate history broadly, to compare the events of one period with those of another, there is
a strong tendency to distortion arising from the point of view.
It is almost as if the difficulty were one of perspective. Sup-

* Joan Grant, *Winged Pharaoh,* New York, Harper and Brothers,
1938.

pose, for instance, the scale of the years is marked along a wall. If you stand in front of the middle of the scale, some distance away, the equal periods of time will be represented by equal distances and by equal angular deviations of view. But if, instead, you stand at the end of the scale and look down it lengthwise, the portions of the scale that are near you will seem very much longer than those that are distant; and near events will seem much more important than the more remote ones. The time scale of human progress is certainly not linear. Technical progress grows more rapid as time goes on, and perhaps the best chronological scale for the history of science and technology would be one in which the divisions of the scale were proportional to the logarithms of their distance from the present time.

Another example of this distortion is that it is impossible for us to understand the effect on human history of the events that are occurring around us.* Our judgment of the importance of the events of the time is very likely to be different from the judgment of history. There comes to mind Anatole France's story of the procurator of Judea, who was visited in retirement by a friend who had known him in Syria. Their conversation strayed on to the events that had occurred when Pontius Pilate had been in office in Jerusalem, and his friend asked him if he remembered a certain Jesus whom he had delivered to crucifixion. Pilate's answer will forever remain the most perfect example of the ironical climax: "Jesus?" he murmured, "Jesus of Nazareth? I can't call him to mind."

History is full of incidents which were ignored by contemporaries but which proved to be of the greatest importance. In 1453, Constantinople was taken by the Turks. The blow was felt throughout Christendom; a European congress was called at Regensburg to promote a crusade, but nobody would come. The organization of Europe had broken down, exhausted with war and quarrels. A contemporary writer said:

* Cf. H. B. Phillips, "On the Nature of Progress," *American Scientist*, **33**, 253 (1945).

"Where is the mortal man who can bring England into accord with France? Let a great host set forth, and its internal enmities will destroy its organization. Behold, a true picture of Christendom." * Few would have been found who realized that the final fall of the Byzantine Empire was far less important than the work of Johannes Gutenberg, who for the first time was printing books from movable type.

At the time when Isaac Newton was preparing the *Principia* for publication, in 1686 and 1687, the British people were engaged in a bitter struggle with the king, arising from the fact that the king was a Catholic, while the people as a whole had become Protestants and after years of struggle had a very great fear and hatred of the Roman Catholic church. The feeling was so bitter that the struggle ended in the expulsion of the king, whose place on the throne was taken by his Dutch son-in-law, William, and his daughter, Mary. It may easily be imagined that in a political crisis of this magnitude few people saw that the work of a professor at Cambridge was of far greater significance for the future of England and of the world. Again in 1831, England was seething with discontent. Even the old Duke of Wellington, the victor of Waterloo, was threatened by the mob. The Reform Bill had been defeated in the House of Commons and a dissolution of Parliament was necessary. In these circumstances, probably no one recognized that the work of Michael Faraday, who in that year discovered the principles of electromagnetic induction, was to change the face of the earth.

There is no absolute standard for the judgment of history. One individual will be interested in history as a record of administration; another, as a record of the art of human welfare; another will view history in relation to economics; a medical man has written two very interesting books on the medical aspects of the history of well-known individuals; in this study we are considering the *progress* of civilization through the ages.

* Boulting, "Aeneas Sylvius," quoted by J. W. Thompson, *The Middle Ages,* p. 205, New York, Alfred A. Knopf, Inc., 1931.

Sarton says: "If we wish to explain the progress of mankind, then we must focus our attention on the development of science and its applications." This view is emphasized by Sarton in his definitions of science and the theorem and corollary he derived from it.* They are:

Definition: Science is systematized positive knowledge, or what has been taken as such at different ages and in different places.

Theorem: The acquisition and systematization of positive knowledge are the only human activities which are truly cumulative and progressive.

Corollary: The history of science is the only history which can illustrate the progress of mankind. In fact, progress has no definite and unquestionable meaning in other fields than the field of science.

Sarton points out that we should not be dazzled by the shibboleth of progress, for there are other features of human life which are at least as precious as scientific activities though they are unprogressive; and he instances charity and the love of beauty. Nevertheless, the scientific activity of man is the only one which is obviously and undoubtedly cumulative and progressive.† As we have seen, the very idea of progress is modern, an idea that derived from the scientific revolution of the seventeenth century and the industrial revolution that followed it.

The justification for selecting scientific knowledge as essentially different from the artistic attainments or the philosophical attainments of man is that scientific knowledge builds on itself. An artist is essentially born. It is true that he acquires a certain amount of technical skill when trained by a master and is influenced by his predecessors, but fundamentally the level of his art is his own, and for that reason the best art of the early periods compares well with art of the later periods.

* George Sarton, *The Study of the History of Science,* p. 5, Cambridge, Harvard University Press, 1936.

† George Sarton, *History of Science and the New Humanism,* p. 10, Cambridge, Harvard University Press, 1937.

What is true of sculpture and architecture is true also of literature. Literature takes different forms in different periods. We may be inclined to value, for instance, the lyric poetry of the recent era. But would we place it above the epic poetry of the classical age or the religious poems of the great period of high civilization which preceded the classical age—from which we have such writing as the *Book of Job* or Akhnaton's *Hymn to the Sun?* The science of the Renaissance, however, started where classical science ended, and classical science was largely based on Egyptian and Babylonian science. Through the ages, while the other activities of man showed no definite progression but merely a growth for a time and then a decline, the level of scientific knowledge steadily increased. As Sarton says: *

> When one reads the history of science one has the exhilarating feeling of climbing a big mountain. The history of art gives one an altogether different impression. It is not at all like the ascension of a mountain, always upward whichever the direction of one's path; it is rather like a leisurely journey across a hilly country. One climbs up to the top of this hill or that, then down into another valley, perhaps a deeper one than any other, then up the next hill, and so forth and so on. An erratic succession of climaxes and anticlimaxes the amplitude of which cannot be predicted.

Let us consider, then, the progress of mankind as illustrated by the history of science or, as I should prefer to say, the history of science and technology, the record of natural knowledge and of invention.

We may divide the history of mankind into great periods, each of which is conditioned by a major invention; and it is possible to carry out this division in many ways, according to the controlling inventions that we select. The following classification seems to form a convenient framework for our discussion:

* *Ibid.*, p. 11.

1. The invention of tools and weapons.
2. The discovery of agriculture.
3. The invention of writing.
4. The invention of printing.

By the first of these inventions man evolved from the animal. Agriculture introduced community life, and from it evolved a structure of society. With writing came the production of records and the transmission, imperfect at first, of knowledge. With the invention of printing, the spreading of knowledge from the writing of one man to become the common heritage of mankind was so enormously facilitated that printing produced a revolutionary change in the rate of progress.

Our record of man opens with the fragments of tools and pots, the tools long before the pots. The tools were made from wood, bone, or flint. The wood has vanished, and few of the early bone tools remain, but the flint tools form a great record—almost the only record we have for the first 40,000 years of the 50,000 during which man has made and used tools. Those first 40,000 years are covered by the paleolithic period; the neolithic period starts at about 10,000 B.C.; and the historical period some time after 5000 B.C.* This earliest record we know—that of the flint weapons and tools made by prehistoric and neolithic man—can be deciphered by the changes and improvements in the tools and by the improvement in the technique by which the tools were made.

Flint is found wherever there are chalk deposits, as there are in many parts of Western Europe. The great nodules of flint are found in cavities in the chalk rock and can easily be obtained by anybody who digs a hole in the ground. There are some places where there are layers of flint that form flint mines, and around these places the ancient men worked so many flints that the whole ground is covered with masses of flakes. If a lump of flint is struck with a sharp

---

* For a modification of this chronology and a discussion of prehistoric chronology, see G. E. Daniel, *The Three Ages,* London, Cambridge University Press, 1943.

blow concentrated at a point, it breaks in such a way that a sort of cap can be lifted off, exposing underneath a double cone. If the blow is dealt on the margin of the block, a flake comes off showing a swelling near the point of impact. This method of working flints is known as "knapping." Because of the durability of flint and the very long period during which flint tools were made, enormous numbers have been found both of the primitive hand axes and scrapers and of the later, more specialized, tools.

In the paleolithic period, improvement in the flint tools was very slow indeed. After a time, however, the craftsmen learned to make finer and more delicate tools—pointed awls for making holes in skins, by which the skins could be fastened together with sinews—and weapons, spearpoints and, later, arrow points. Then the art of knapping improved as a result of the discovery that small flakes could be detached accurately by pressure, so that the coarse serrations could be subdivided and a much finer edge obtained, and then the flints were polished and a smooth edge obtained by grinding. At this time, other arts developed, and the whole cultural period is distinguished from the paleolithic period by calling it "neolithic."

Our knowledge of the history of that vast period of man's activity depends upon the study of the progress of flint work. It is quite probable that different stages in the art of working flint did not occur contemporaneously in different countries, so that in one part of the world man may have been making paleolithic instruments, while in another part the flint craftsmen had learned the neolithic art. Generally, however, the occurrence of closely similar flint implements in different places is held to indicate that the cultures were contemporaneous. Flinders Petrie, for instance, considers that the identity of flints from the Fayum of Egypt with Solutrean flints from Western Europe indicates that the beginning of his sequence dating was contemporaneous with the Solutrean paleolithic period.

At some period between 10,000 and 5000 B.C., we find that the people of the new stone age were appearing in Egypt and Mesopotamia with their improved tools and also with other inventions—pottery and agriculture. Besides tools and weapons, primitive man needed cooking utensils and still more, perhaps, he needed jars in which he could carry and keep water. Baskets were made very early. Stone jars also were made, but they required much labor when made by primitive tools. It was not a great step, though it was a very important invention, to think of daubing the baskets with mud and making them more or less waterproof. Probably the discovery that the mud became much more waterproof if it were baked in the fire was made accidentally. There were plenty of open hearths in which a mud-daubed basket might be left. At any rate, the earliest pots seem to have had the mud-smeared basket as their ancestor. Later pots could be made without the basketwork by baking the mud itself, molded to shape, but those earliest pots still bear the marks of their origin in the tracings of basketlike lines with which they are decorated.

And at that point, art entered the everyday world. The pots could be decorated with mud of different colors and with designs of intricate fancy. These patterns and working methods were so stable that by means of them the cultures of the neolithic and early bronze ages can be classified. We see the steady improvement in the skill and fancy with which the pots were formed, so that instead of depending upon the classification of the flint tools, we can introduce approximate datings for given periods from the potsherds with which every ancient city is necessarily covered, pots being what they are and children what they have always been.

A good example of the use of pottery in constructing a time scale for material revealed by excavation is given by Petrie in his dating of the remains of prehistoric Egypt. In this work, he selected a thousand graves with at least five forms of pottery in each. Then a card slip was used for each grave with the content specified, and every occurrence of a type of pottery was examined and compared with the other examples. This process of comparison resulted in bringing the thousand graves into a connected order in time, each grave as a general rule containing some of the pottery of the graves near it in the order but not containing pots of those that were more distant in the order. The whole series of graves could be divided into fifty parts, and these were numbered arbitrarily from 30 to 80 in order to leave space for later discoveries of graves that might not fit into the sequence and that might have to be placed before or after those that had been examined. In this way, a definite sequence dating could be made for the graves and, therefore, for the pottery and other material found in the graves, ending with the graves of the historical dynasties for which chronological dates were known. The same method has been applied to the dating of the different levels of excavation in Mesopotamia and Syria. Indeed, our knowledge of prehistoric Mesopotamia is almost entirely dependent on dating by means of pottery.

At this stage in the history of civilization, when men had the good tools of the neolithic age and pots hardened in the fire, a new factor of fundamental importance appeared—the second of the great inventions of mankind.

Agriculture was probably discovered by the women, who gathered the seeds of plants while their men hunted animals. One day they must have realized that seeds could be sown artificially and that, if they waited long enough, seeds produced a crop. With the coming of agriculture came real civilization. Men ceased to be nomads. They settled in villages; and those villages were naturally along the river valleys, where there was mud, in which the seeds could be planted, and water, necessary for plant growth.

There, in the villages or, rather, in the towns into which the villages had grown, came the third great invention—writing. And with writing, the period of prehistory ends and history commences. Man began to write five or six thousand years ago. Those who study the river valleys of Mesopotamia

claim that writing had its origin there, but it certainly originated independently in Egypt, and the Egyptologists are by
no means willing to concede the claims of their archaeological
rivals.

In our study of history after the invention of writing, we
are less dependent on material relics and can use the records.
However, we are still interested in tracing the history
of civilization in terms of its arts and crafts, in the tools,
weapons, and ornaments that ancient man produced and left
behind him, although we have available generally from the
early periods only that small fraction of the production which
was buried in the graves.

Having summarized the progress of man through the prehistoric period until the invention of the written record, let
us endeavor to look at the history of civilization as a whole
and consider the nature of the phenomena it displays, in the
same way that we should consider any other group of natural
phenomena.

Any contemplation of the pattern of history gives at once
an impression of cyclic change—of the rise, flowering, and
fall of local civilizations of peoples and of empires. Many
empires have risen to power and fallen again in the last 5000
years. Some had a very brief triumph, like that of Attila
the Hun or Alaric the Goth or, much more recently, of the
Swedish Empire, which for a short time ruled all northeast-
ern Europe. Others lasted much longer, the maximum duration being the 3000 years which the Egyptian system endured.

Indeed, when we contemplate Egyptian history we get the
impression of cyclic rise and fall within the life of that country, suggesting that this cyclic structure is not connected with
the individual nation, race, or empire but with the period of
time, and that the long duration of the Egyptian system
enables us to discern within that duration several cycles.
Thus, from the prehistoric beginnings of Egypt, we find a
rapid advance in architecture and sculpture to the time of
the pyramid builders in the Fourth Dynasty, corresponding
approximately to 3000 B.C. The artistic level of the architec-

ture and sculpture of the Fourth Dynasty is considered by many students to be equal to any that has been reached by man, and the engineering work of the men who built the pyramids shows an enormous development in technical skill which was not exceeded for thousands of years. After the great flowering of the Old Kingdom, as it is called, the level of culture in Egypt slowly decayed. There was a period of decadence, of bad and weak government, with the introduction of a feudal period, in which the land was governed, and too often misgoverned, by local barons. It was the first recorded period of depression, and it was recognized as such by the writers of that time. Then, about 2100 B.C., the Middle Kingdom of Egypt rose in all its glory, producing not only a great renaissance of art but also the building, as Herodotus tells us, of the most prodigious palace ever erected by man— that great building which Herodotus says was greater than all the temples of Greece put together. Then again came darkness, this time from the invasion of the Hyksos, who seized the throne of Egypt. Again a king from the south restored the power of the Egyptians and founded the great Eighteenth Dynasty, which ended in a blaze of glory in 1350 B.C. Part of its treasure was buried in the grave of Tutankhamen. Then the long degeneration of Egypt started and continued until, with the invasions of the Assyrians and of the Persians, Egypt fell, never to rise again. Thus, within the recorded history of Egypt, there are three great cycles, their maxima corresponding approximately to 3000 B.C., 2000 B.C., and 1500 B.C.; and following each of these maxima there was a period of depression and decay.

In 1911, Sir Flinders Petrie wrote a little book that he entitled *The Revolutions of Civilization*.* In this book he uses his great knowledge of ancient history and, especially, of the history of Egypt to develop a general interpretation of history. He says:

* W. M. Flinders Petrie, *The Revolutions of Civilization*, Harper's, 1911, reprinted by Peter Smith, New York, 1941.

Can we extract a meaning from all the ceaseless turmoil and striving, and success and failure, of these thousands of years? Can we see any regular structure behind it all? Can we learn any general principles that may formulate the past, or be projected on the mists of the future? . . . Hitherto the comparatively brief outlook of Western history has given us only the great age of classical civilization before modern times. We have been in the position of a child that remembers only a single summer before that which he enjoys. To such an one the cold, dark, miserable winter that has intervened seems a needless and inexplicable interruption of a happier order—of a summer which should never cease. Only a few years ago a writer of repute deplored the mysterious fall of the Roman Empire, which in his view ought to have been always prosperous, and never have fallen to the barbarians. He was the child who could not understand the winter. From what we now know, it is evident, even on the most superficial view, that civilization is an intermittent phenomenon.

Thus throughout history Petrie finds that cycles of civilization have succeeded each other. In each cycle, the phases are marked by similar characteristics which may be detected by studying the products of the period. Each cycle has its period of preparation, shown essentially in art as archaism; then a period of maturity; and, finally, a period of decline and decadence, to be followed by the archaic period of the next cycle. Petrie uses the simile of summer and winter for the growth and fall of civilization and points out that this analogy of the Great Year was familiar to the ancients. Petrie uses as the most valuable index of the cyclic change the development of sculpture, largely because it is more permanent than other products of handicraft. He points out, however, that sculpture "is only one, and not the most important, of the many subjects that might be compared throughout the various ages." [But] "it is available over so long a period in so many countries." He adds to sculpture in his survey some discussion of painting, music, mechanics, wealth, and even political developments. It is remarkable that he lays little stress on the development of technology.

In the last ten thousand years, covering the neolithic and historic periods, Petrie finds evidence of eight cycles, of which the first two were found in prehistoric Egypt; then four, covering the whole dynastic period of Egypt; and, last, the classic and western European cycles. Each cycle starts with an archaic period characterized particularly by the careful working of detail without treating it as an integral part of the whole. The rise from archaism to maturity is almost always rapid, and, after a period of maturity, decline sets in, characterized by a tendency to stiffness and conventionality and a slow worsening and degradation of the style.

The most familiar cycle is, of course, that of the classical period. We have the archaic Greek statues of the sixth century B.C., followed by the great classical period of maturity in the late fifth and fourth centuries, and then the transformation into the Hellenistic period, followed by the long decay through Roman times. To some extent, perhaps, this cycle is complicated by a revival in the Roman period, accompanied by a copying of the Greek classical works by the Roman sculptors.

If the classical period alone were known to us, we should dismiss the whole matter as being peculiar to the historical events of that period; and this is generally done by historians trained primarily in classical history. But the Egyptian evidence for the existence of parallel cycles in sculpture is overwhelming. The same type of cycle can be traced, for instance, in Petrie's fourth period—that of the pyramid builders—in the rise of the archaic sculpture, the freedom of the sculpture and architecture of the Fourth Dynasty, the slow decline through the Fifth and Sixth Dynasties, and the collapse of the sculpture as the feudal system displaced the centralized government of the Old Kingdom. A new archaic sculpture then came into evidence, rising to the maturity of Petrie's fifth period in the Twelfth Dynasty, and then deteriorated, disappearing with the invasion of the Hyksos. The sixth period cycle is that of the New Kingdom, where the period of decline was very prolonged and was marked by the great temple group built by the Ramesside rulers. To see the difference between the artistic levels in maturity and in the decline, one has only to compare Hatshepsut's temple at Deir el Bahri with the great hall at Karnak built three hundred years later.

To determine the duration of these periods, Petrie selects the best-defined position in each cycle of the development of art as the close of the archaic age in sculpture. This is best defined, of course, because of the rapid improvement that is generally noted at this stage; and, by means of it, there is possible some appreciation of the period between the waves of art in successive cycles. Petrie believes that the average period is about thirteen hundred years. It must be remembered, however, that Petrie's early chronology is not accepted by other scholars and that it is generally agreed that his dates before 1600 B.C. need correction. If we use the chronology generally accepted now, Petrie's chart gives five complete periods in four thousand years, an average of eight hundred years per cycle.*

By making judgments for subjects other than sculpture, Petrie found that painting and literature tended to reach their climax later than sculpture. He draws a chart in which the different periods are shown as if they were on the surface of a cylinder, each period ending, of course, at the date at which the next period began. In this chart, the points that he has marked for sculpture, painting, literature, mechanics, and wealth tend to diverge, each of them coming later as the cycles progress. If this chart is redrawn with the early chronology changed to accord with that accepted by J. H. Breasted and other modern scholars—3000 B.C. as the beginning of the Third Dynasty and 1800 B.C. as the end of the Twelfth Dynasty—it becomes that shown in Figure 1. Interpolating the new dates derived from those selected by Petrie for the end of the archaic style in sculpture in each cycle, we get the zigzag line shown. It is no longer possible to draw a

* But the modified chart shown in Figure 2, p. 34, gives a duration of five hundred years per cycle.

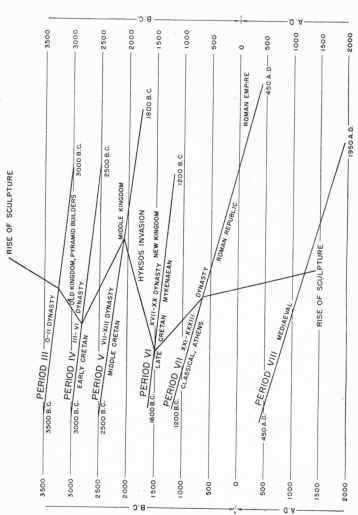

FIGURE 1.   Petrie's Chart of Historical Cycles.   (Redrawn and Redated.)

straight line for sculpture, and the cycles clearly differ in length, the early ones lasting only about five hundred years, while the classical and medieval cycles last sixteen hundred and fifty and fifteen hundred years, respectively.

The long cycles can very probably be corrected by consideration of the historical facts. The classical cycle in Greece did not start in 1200 B.C.; at any rate, it did not start at any level corresponding to that existing in Egypt in 1200 B.C. If we put the beginning of the Greek classical cycle at 800 B.C., and its end at 200 B.C., with the defeat of Macedon by Rome, we get a cycle of normal length, which can be followed by a Roman cycle of six hundred and fifty years, starting with the destruction of Carthage and ending with the fall of Rome. The course of art in the Roman cycle is naturally affected by the persistence of Greek architecture and statuary. Similarly, we can accept a discontinuity between the Roman and the medieval cycles and give the latter its beginning in A.D. 1000 and its end in A.D. 1700, a length of seven hundred years. If we accept these modifications of Petrie's later cycles, we get the chart shown in Figure 2.

In an article in *Antiquity*, Collingwood discusses Petrie's book and questions the value of his standards of artistic achievement.* He points out that what Petrie calls decadent another critic of art might consider beautiful. For example, he holds that the Byzantine grave stele of Bellicia (Figure 3), which Petrie classifies as occurring in the period of degradation between the classical and medieval periods, shows vigor of drawing and an "unearthly" beauty, and he considers that it is unfair to compare its beauty with that of a classical stele, since it cannot be compared either as superior or inferior but only different; that is, Collingwood claims that "beauty is in the eye of the beholder," and that there are no fixed standards by which art at different times can be compared. He says, in fact, that not only are there no dark ages except in the sense in which every age is dark, and that there are ages

* R. G. Collingwood, "The Theory of Historical Cycles and Progress," *Antiquity*, **II**, 435 (1927).

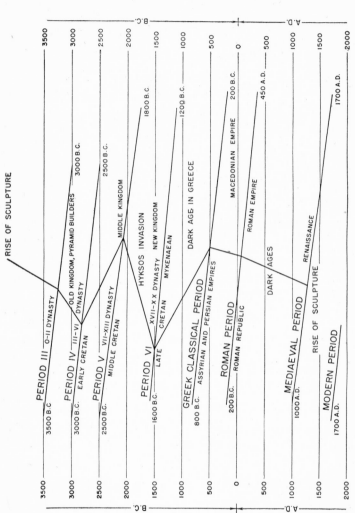

FIGURE 2.   Chart of Historical Cycles.   (Revised.)

that individual historians dislike and misunderstand, but
there are also no decadences.   Thus Collingwood argues that
the cyclical view of history is a function of the limitation of
historical knowledge.   History appears to consist of discon-
nected episodes, but, if we had more knowledge, we should

FIGURE 3.   The Stele of Bellicia.   (From Petrie's *The Revolutions of
Civilization,* published by Peter Smith, New York, 1941.)

see that the episodes were connected; and he feels that Petrie
sees the structure of history as imposed by the historian view-
ing the scene and not inherent in the facts.

This view does not seem to accord with the real situation.
Petrie's cycles are not based on the view of beauty adopted
by the onlooker; they are based largely on a technical matter,
the skill shown in execution.   A critic might endorse the
scribblings of a child or the primitive work of a Negro in the
forest as representing a degree of beauty which entitled them
to be considered excellent art, but there is no doubt that the

ability of the child or of the primitive Negro to reproduce line and form is low. In the same way, the ability of artists to draw or of sculptors to design and carve or of architects to design and build has varied at different periods. Their technical skill is not constant. The artist who drew the stele of Bellicia may have drawn it in that form because he thought it was beautiful, but it is absurd to imagine that that artist was the equal in technical skill of the artist who carved the Attic tombstones of the fifth and fourth centuries B.C. It is very easy in a country like Egypt, where the standards of judgments did not vary, to observe the variation in the technical ability of the painters, sculptors, and architects. The carvings in the tombs show mastery over the subject, which increased as the cycle progressed, and then the style became limited and stiff and conventional as decadence set in. This is not a change in objective; the objects represented are the same. It is a change in skill, in the mastery of the art. In the decadent stage it is not uncommon to find that the artists copied the designs of an earlier period because they recognized that they had not the ability to originate designs of the same quality as those which they were copying.

If, then, we accept Petrie's view of the existence of these cultural cycles, let us follow his discussion of their origin. After considering the effects of changes of climate, which have often produced migrations of peoples, Petrie considers that the rise of a new civilization is conditioned by the immigration of a different people; that is to say, it arises from a mixture of two different stocks. The effective mixture cannot take place all at once. When a new stock migrates into a country, usually in a military invasion, there is an appreciable barrier between the two races. But such barriers always give way in time when the two races are in contact, and in seven or eight centuries the two races are completely blended. Petrie concludes, therefore, that the cycle is started by the invasion of a new stock, which introduces an archaic period superimposed on the decadent style of the previous cycle, and then, as the new stock blends with the old, artistic and social development increases until the maximum is reached. For most of the cycles discussed by Petrie, the migration of a new stock appears to be a historical fact. The dynastic people of Egypt, for instance, initiated Petrie's fourth cycle, in which the peak was reached in the Fourth Dynasty; people from the south, that of the Twelfth Dynasty; the Hyksos invasion and the people of Thebes represent the new blood for the New Kingdom cycle; the Doric invasion of Greece initiated the classical cycle; and the influx of peoples into the Roman Empire, the medieval cycle.

The origin of cycles is discussed in a very interesting article by O. G. S. Crawford.* Starting with Petrie's idea that the development of a new phase of civilization depends upon the crossing of two stocks having their own cultures, Crawford pursues a biological analogy, comparing Petrie's different stocks with different varieties of animals and concluding with a generalization that each phase of civilization has a life of its own and may be regarded as if it were a species composed of living creatures. Thus the life of each phase corresponds to the life of a species as a whole; the units composing the phases at any moment of history correspond to the individuals composing the species; and a phase, therefore, is born and passes through maturity to decline and extinction, just as does an individual. The idea is not new. Crawford quotes Sir Arthur Keith, who says: "The resemblance between the body physiological and the body politic is more than an analogy; it is a reality." †

Just as a multicellular organism evolves from a single cell, so the cultural community has evolved from free-roving individuals or small groups, this occurring, as has already been pointed out, with the introduction of agriculture, when the nomads settled at one point and founded communities. This very operation can be observed occurring today, when the

---

* O. G. S. Crawford, "Historical Cycles," *Antiquity,* **V,** 5 (1931).

† Sir Arthur Keith, *Concerning Man's Origin,* New York, G. P. Putnam's Sons, 1928.

Bedouin of the desert have settled down into communities in Trans-Jordan as cultivators of the soil. And it is interesting to notice that the fact that the cultivators are of the same tribes as the Bedouin does not preserve them from raiding by the nomads. With the integration of the individual into a cultural community, subdivision of function develops, just as the single cells develop special functions in the multicellular organisms. Crawford concludes that, looking at the process as a whole, we can see that life evolves in a spiral. It begins with a single cell. After many ages of development, an organism is evolved that finally becomes a human being. Human beings may be considered to be, in turn, the units of organized nations that will evolve until they, in turn, become the units or individuals of yet another society, this last being, perhaps, the world state from which those races and social systems that cannot be incorporated will eventually die out. The idea of a society as an organism is to be found, of course, in Spencer's synthetic philosophy; and the ideas that Crawford discusses are dealt with formally in J. Needham's *Herbert Spencer Lecture.**

Leaving these wider speculations, we may ask: What is the value of this cyclic theory to a student of history? When we study a comparatively brief period of ancient history, it is impossible to understand its relation to any general scheme of world history. But if we accept the idea that civilization moves in cycles, we can place any brief period in relation to the events that preceded and followed it. As Petrie says, the interpretation of the later Roman Empire is quite different according to whether one assumes that the fall of Rome was a unique phenomenon or whether one feels that the fall of Rome was really one manifestation of the long decadence of the classical cycle, to be followed eventually by the archaic period of the Middle Ages and the revival of the western cycle. When discussing Roman law in *Aspects of Social Be-*

* J. Needham, "Integrative Levels," p. 233, *Time, the Refreshing River,* London, George Allen and Unwin, 1943.

*havior,** Frank finds it necessary to argue against the assumption that Roman law had behind it nothing but a development from a most primitive culture and reminds his readers that the human race had existed many thousands of years before the reign of Romulus. He complains of some evolutionists, who write "as though Homer had just bid good-bye to a grandfather who hung by a tail from a Thracian oak tree." †

The cyclic theory is of value, however, not only as a guide to the thinking of the historian but also as a suggestion to the modern philosopher. In an essay on modernism, Raymond Dexter Havens expresses his uneasiness at the trend of art. ‡ He finds himself unhappy in a world in which Picasso is one of the most esteemed of living artists, Schönberg and Hindemuth are representatives of music, and James Joyce and E. E. Cummings are leaders of literature, though he finally braces himself to accept his fate and to see what he can make of God in these "modern" methods of expression. But this type of art is not really modern; there are many examples of it in the past. If Picasso and many of his followers had painted in the sixth century, we should have classified the work very simply as decadent. Epstein's sculpture would have been in its natural home in Greece during the Byzantine period or, for that matter, in Thebes in the ninth century B.C. Art is not moving downwards permanently; it is merely moving through the decadent stages of its cycle. And just as the archaic and classical periods followed the decadent Egyptian work of the ninth century B.C. and architecture in Europe developed from that of the sixth century to its glorious maximum in the early Gothic of the twelfth, so there will again be artists who can depict natural objects and writers who can explain what they mean.

* Tenney Frank, *Aspects of Social Behavior,* Cambridge, Harvard University Press, 1932.

† This shows the danger of a classicist using scientific analogies. Monkeys with prehensile tails are unknown in the Eastern Hemisphere!

‡ Raymond Dexter Havens, *The Burden of Incertitude,* Rochester, University of Rochester, 1944.

In spite of the repetition of the rise and fall of art, of literature, and even of civilization as a whole, mankind has made progress through recorded history. Cities and empires have risen, and cities and empires have fallen. Artists, engineers, and philosophers have lived and worked, died and been forgotten, but none the less, some systematic secular change has occurred. If the circle has come its full round, the pattern of history is a spiral, not a ring, for the start of a new cycle of civilization is never identical with that of the last; and, on the average, each cycle starts from a point a little above that of the preceding cycle, so that the successive turns of the spiral are not coplanar, and the pattern may be more accurately depicted as a helix.* All through the paleolithic period, little change occurred. Nevertheless, there came a time when the production of the flint tools improved, and we recognize that this phase lies above that of the preceding phase, a change recognized by the term "neolithic" instead of "paleolithic." Then somewhat more rapid progress is made; and in one or two more turns of the helix we reach the point where agriculture is discovered, where the villages and towns come into being, and then where writing is invented. And now successive turns rise more rapidly from each other, and we see that it is necessary to consider the meaning of this vertical component of our diagram.

Since time is represented by the angular co-ordinate, the vertical component must be the level of achievement, different according to the field of accomplishment selected—sculpture, architecture, engineering skill, literature, and so forth. This is the level of civilization as a whole and not that of any single component. In many fields, there is little or no secular improvement—in the art of sculpture, for instance—and there must, therefore, be some factor in the vertical component of the helix that has steadily increased and

* The frontispiece is an attempt to realize this graphically. It is a photograph of a helix of wire. The lower coils are close together, and, as they rise, they are distorted and even overlap, but finally the vertical component increases rapidly.

now determines the progress of civilization as a whole. This component can only be that of progress in the field in which, according to Sarton, it has definite and unquestionable meaning, that of "systematized, positive knowledge," that is, Science.

Through the ages we see an increase in man's understanding of nature and his control of natural forces. Astronomy started as astrology, but this involved the observation of the positions of the heavenly bodies and thus led to the astronomical determination of time and the establishment of a calendar. Moreover, from observations of the stars it was possible to form an idea of world geography; and this made possible the development of navigation away from the coasts. Practical metallurgy led into chemistry, for which alchemy played the part that astrology played for astronomy. Through a vast amount of suffering man attained some knowledge of anatomy, because of his need for surgery, and finally of physiology. Thus, step by step, science advanced through the ages until we reached the seventeenth century. Then there was a sudden and definite change in the rate of learning. The experimental method of research was discovered, and the advance in scientific method and knowledge suddenly became much more rapid. The cause and nature of this sudden change are discussed later. Indeed, the nature of science and the methods of experimental inquiry form the principal subjects of this book. In the meantime, we may complete our picture of the helix of history by realizing that it shows a steady increase in the separation of the coils and then, suddenly, after the discovery of the methods of experimental science, springs upward in an almost vertical direction.

Chapter III

THE METHOD OF SCIENCE

In the previous chapter the great pageant of the historical past was discussed, in which we can trace the growth of scientific knowledge, which has followed the rise and fall of civilization but which, nevertheless, has increased as time has gone on, so that it has been the index of all man's progress.

Now let us consider the nature and origin of this scientific knowledge. But first it is necessary to revise and clarify the implications of some earlier statements. Progress in civilization has been said to correspond to an increase in scientific knowledge and to its application to the social and economic life of the time. Up to the present, science and technology have been treated as synonymous; but we find upon investigation that they do not have a common origin.

Scientific knowledge arises from certain characteristics in the mind of man which cause him to seek to understand phenomena. Technology arises from an entirely different motive—the desire to acquire more or better things. The flint knapper was not a scientist; he was a technologist, and he proceeded by the immemorial method of technology—practice and invention. The science of flint knapping would involve a study of the structure of the flint, of those properties which produce the conchoidal fracture characteristic of the substance, and this was far beyond the ability of anybody who wished to make flints for practical use as tools. In practice, technology advances to an astonishing extent in the absence of any accurate knowledge of the principles on which it is based. When the modern building contractor undertakes the erection of a building, he makes a survey of the materials he will need and arranges for the delivery of the

42

necessary quantity as required. But a primitive builder will fetch his materials as he wants them, obtaining more and more until the building is finished, without any preliminary survey of the quantity required. Modern industry makes use of statistical surveys and cost analysis. Only a few years ago such aids to operation were unknown. Such matters have no relation to the technical skill of the craftsman; the builders of the Pyramids and the goldsmiths who wrought the coffin of Tutankhamen were craftsmen of superb skill, but they probably did little calculating before they started work.

Technology has usually proceeded by trial and error. The practice of photography, for instance, preceded any knowledge of the theory of the photographic process. Photographic materials were made by trial, and to this day the making of photographic materials is in advance of the understanding of the basic science of the subject. Advances in photographic science have provided a working theory of the light sensitivity of photographic materials, of what happens to them during exposure, and of what happens to them during development. But the relationship between the operations of making the photographic emulsion and the properties of the resultant emulsion is not yet understood. Only a few years ago practically nothing was known of the way in which certain dyes sensitize silver bromide in photographic emulsions to the regions of the spectrum which the dyes absorb. The matter is being elucidated, but ignorance of it did not prevent our discovering great numbers of dyes and applying them to the sensitizing of silver bromide.

There comes a point in technology, however, where progress is slow or even stops for lack of knowledge of the fundamental science. Progress in photography has been greatly accelerated by our understanding the physical chemistry underlying the photographic process.

Progress in engineering is dependent to a very great extent on fundamental physics, on which all engineering is based. But the invention of the steam engine was not dependent upon the understanding of Newton's work, nor was the development of the gasoline engine dependent upon the understanding of Carnot's cycle. It is easier to improve engines if you understand thermodynamics; but the men who invented the engines did not understand thermodynamics, and many of those who improved them almost to the present level did so without any knowledge of the scientific principles which underlay their work. The greatest inventor of all time, Thomas A. Edison, was not a scientist and was not even interested in science. He was interested in doing things and not in understanding how he could do them. Nevertheless, the advance of technology has been greatly stimulated by the advance of scientific knowledge and, to a considerable extent, has been made possible by that advance. Edison, for instance, observed the *Edison effect;* that is, from a glowing filament in a lamp, a current would pass through the vacuum to a second filament in the same lamp. But Edison was not interested in studying this further or, at any rate, did not do so, and it was left for Owen Richardson to show the origin of the current and for J. A. Fleming and his successors to design the electronic tubes, on which so much of our recent electrotechnology is based. The whole technology of electricity is based on scientific discoveries, and without those discoveries the technologists would probably never have applied electrical methods, because there is no convenient source of electricity in nature except the intractable lightning flash and the phenomena of static electricity, which have even at present very little application in practice.

Technology even today proceeds by trial and error, the experimental method, but as a result of our knowledge of pure science, we have learned to experiment more actively and more efficiently. Science suggests to the technologist experiments by means of which progress can be made. Technology is not an offspring of science; it is a separate activity of mankind, but it is very much stimulated by the other human activities of scientific study and research.

The special activity of mankind which we call *science* began as a classification of facts. Certain types of men have a desire to classify facts into patterns, to associate facts with each other and thus understand, as they would say, the connections between the facts. This understanding usually arises from repetition of the same facts in the same order. There is no difficulty, for instance, in associating the phenomenon of rain with the presence of clouds, and one of the earliest facts of which man was aware must have been that rain comes from the clouds. It was much later, however, when he realized that lightning and thunder were also natural phenomena associated with the clouds; and primitive man does not seem to have associated them at all with rain.

The beginnings of science, then, are to be found in a system of classification in which different facts are associated and regarded as being in the same classification or, as it is usually put, as being due to the same cause. Very often, early man was wrong in his classification, and his association of facts proved later to be incorrect; such incorrect associations have persisted through the ages. When such incorrect associations have been held by many men for many years, we often call them *superstitions,* and they become so rooted in our minds that they are very difficult to eradicate.

One of the most interesting systems of incorrect association of facts is known as *magic.* One of the earliest facts of which an animal becomes conscious is that its own body is not functioning normally. Usually the trouble corrects itself and the animal recovers. As soon as man began to reason, he must have tried to find remedies for his bodily disorders; and those remedies were associated with his daily routine and especially, perhaps, with food. If a plant can make you ill, cannot the same plant or another make you well? If you eat the same plant, you are using a homeopathic medicine; if you eat a different plant, an allopathic medicine. If you simply hang the plant around your neck, you are employing magic. In so far as men have knowledge, they use that knowledge. Where knowledge fails, they attempt to supply it, and we term the attempt magic. Thus, in the medical works of the Egyptians, anatomical and surgical knowledge and the diagnosis and treatment of disease are intermingled with magical spells. Among primitive peoples, magic has always played a great part, and it is perhaps a little difficult for us to realize how deeply the principles of magic are entrenched in the thought and history of man.

Sir J. G. Frazer * analyzes the principles on which magic is based: first, that like produces like or that an effect resembles its cause; and, second, that things which have once been in contact with each other continue to act on each other at a distance. From the first of these principles, which he calls the *law of similarity*, it is inferred that a man can produce any effect he desires merely by imitating it. If a savage, for instance, wants a good crop, he will take care to have it sown by a woman who has many children; or, if a witch doctor, as the practitioners of primitive magic are called, wants to hurt a man, he will make an image of him and then destroy it in the belief that just as the image suffers, so does the man, and when it perishes, he must die. From the second principle, it is inferred that whatever is done to a material object will affect any person with whom the object was once in contact. Most savages are very careful to burn any hair they cut off or the parings of their nails, lest an enemy might use them to do them harm. And in some African tribes, anything once touched by the king must be carefully destroyed. The negative principle, corresponding to the principle of similarity, is the great widespread law of taboo, which governs the things that a man abstains from doing lest, on the principle that like produces like, they should spoil his luck. The Eskimo boys, for instance, are forbidden to play cat's cradle because if they do so their fingers might in later life become entangled in the harpoon line. The principles of magic are so widespread that almost all the acts of primitive peoples are connected with the production of good luck or with the avoidance of ill luck. These widespread principles are by no means extinct among us today.

* J. G. Frazer, *The Golden Bough*, p. 11, one-volume edition, New York, The Macmillan Company, 1922.

On careful analysis many of our beliefs will be found to be essentially magical in origin though we are generally no longer conscious of the sources from which those beliefs have sprung. Malinowski * considers that Frazer overstresses the ritual aspect of magic and that it is the practical aspect of magic as an answer to necessity that explains its persistence. A sick man or a bereaved woman feels that something must be done to assuage the hurt; and, if no effective remedy is available from knowledge, magic takes its place.

An even greater factor than magic in the history of man has been the development of religion. Very early man observed that his food and well-being were closely connected with natural phenomena, such as the cycle of the seasons, which we know to be due to the movement of the earth around the sun. He, however, catalogued the facts that he knew under the hypothesis that natural phenomena were due to the actions of intelligent beings made in his image; and he gave these invented beings jurisdiction over groups of natural phenomena, so that there were gods of the earth, the sky, the sea, and minor gods of trees, rivers, and mountains. Sometimes psychological phenomena were classified in the same way. There were gods of love and war, of terror and sorrow, and thus was built up the structure of religion. When the great prophets came—Buddha, Jesus, and Mohammed— their philosophy drew on this structure and their followers incorporated much of the earlier religious belief in the systems of philosophy that were founded on their teaching. To-day, among what we term *religious beliefs,* we continually encounter groups of associations that started as hypotheses to be used in the classification of natural phenomena. Christian hymns still repeat the belief that the crash of sound that follows the discharge of electricity from a cloud to earth is the voice of a god. But basically religion fulfills a need that men have always felt, the need for knowledge of the fundamental issues of existence. How did the world come into

* B. Malinowski, *A Scientific Theory of Culture,* p. 199, Chapel Hill, University of North Carolina Press, 1944.

being?　Whence did man come?　And where does he go after death?　These are the problems of religion that differ from magic in subject matter,* since magic relates to the specific problems of everyday life—to health and sickness and the supply of food and water.

Bit by bit, in spite of mistakes and false starts, man succeeded in building up a series of associations among the facts he knew that bore the only test having any value, that of confirmation by direct observation or experiment.　Throughout the greater portion of recorded history, the material from which scientific conclusions were drawn was the observation of naturally occurring facts.　Astronomy was, of course, derived purely from observation.　Medicine in the sense of anatomy and pathology was the observation of the structure of the body and of disease.　The experimental sciences were almost non-existent before the seventeenth century, when direct experiments were made to ascertain facts that could not be observed without such experiments.　As we have already seen, it was the development of experimental science that produced changes in the evolution of society that were so startling compared with those that had occurred previously.

The method of science is the accumulation of facts, partly by direct observation of naturally occurring phenomena—aided, of course, by all the instrumental appliances that have been developed to assist the use of the senses—and partly by the production of new facts as the result of direct experiment. These facts are then classified in such a way as to show their interrelations and coincidences and are built up into a body of ideas that are considered valid by the experts in the subject.　This body of ideas is itself the *science* of which they form the material.　Thus the science of physics consists of a group of physical ideas accepted as valid by physicists; the same is true for chemistry, for biology, and the other sciences. These groups of ideas are undergoing constant change.　As new facts accumulate, they are integrated into the old ideas

---

* Malinowski, *loc. cit.*

or, if necessary, into new ideas; sometimes new facts force the revision and change of accepted ideas. The methods used in different branches of science are to some extent peculiar to each, and the tests required to justify the acceptance of an idea as valid are selected by those working in each branch. Thus, as Polanyi says, "Science consists of autonomous branches, ruled by their several systems of ideas; each of these is continuously producing new minor propositions suitable for scientific verification; and by these verifications they are being steadily strengthened and revised." *

The methods of scientific research are analyzed by W. H. George in his book, *The Scientist in Action*.† He defines scientific research as a form of human action, and science, that is, ordered knowledge, as a product of the activity of human beings. But it is not a product of the activity of all human beings; it is only a special and very limited class of human beings who can produce scientific knowledge.

The first qualification of a scientist is often said to be curiosity, that is, a scientist is interested in the observation of facts; but this alone does not distinguish scientists. If it did, there would be far more scientists than there are, since curiosity is a very common characteristic of human beings. A scientist not only observes facts but has an instinctive desire to classify them and set them in order. It is by this classification of facts that science progresses.

The mere observation of facts is not by any means a simple operation. To be of value, facts must be generally received by different observers as true or acceptable; and this, of course, accords with the practice of scientific research, that facts about which there is any doubt must be checked by different observers and discrepancies must be reconciled. If various observers cannot agree as to the facts, it is customary

* M. Polanyi, *Rights and Duties of Science,* p. 175, the Manchester School of Economic and Social Studies, Manchester, England, October 1939.

† W. H. George, *The Scientist in Action,* London, Williams and Norgate, Ltd., 1936.

to put those facts in what we may term a "suspense account," reserving judgment of their validity until a consensus by qualified observers is reached. In the history of science, many observations have been published that were not accepted immediately as accurate. Some of them were later agreed to be erroneous; many were confirmed by further study.

A requirement for this agreement between different observers is that they be critical of the method of observation employed. It is well known to psychologists, for instance, that the reports of different observers of a series of incidents may disagree. George quotes an experiment by A. W. P. Wolters * in which a disorderly incident was deliberately introduced into the middle of a lecture he was giving on observation. The students were then asked to write at once a detailed account of what had occurred. An accurate and full report would have contained ten essential points of detail. The average number of points correctly reported was 3.5, and the reports contained many completely false statements, it being impossible for some of the details to have occurred in that particular room. The cause of these discrepancies is, of course, the unanticipated nature of the events. Reliable observations can be obtained only if the observer is paying attention to the action observed. The more suddenly the phenomenon happens and the more unexpected it is, the less likely are reliable observations to be made.

A second factor in observation is that the observer will see more if he is not only looking *at* what is to be observed, but looking *for* it. A histological section under a microscope will convey no information to one who is ignorant of minute anatomy. I recall once studying an x-ray photograph on an illuminator. The photograph had been taken as a test of the photographic plate. Some one looking over my shoulder said: "Isn't that a beautiful photograph?" To this I replied

* George, *op. cit.*, p. 79.

at once: "I was thinking it was very bad." We were, of course, observing different things. He was interested in the general appearance of the radiograph and would have been equally pleased with any photograph of the same subject. I was critically observing the rendering of detail in the shadows, in which respect that particular photographic material was unsatisfactory.

Observations must be controlled by knowledge of the errors which the sense organ itself may introduce in the observation. The whole class of optical illusions, for instance, may produce false conclusions. The unaided ear, and especially the untrained ear, cannot be trusted to give reliable information as to sounds. There is also the question of personal error. The observer must recognize what H. G. Wells calls "the limitations of the instrument," not only as regards the sense organ but also, as Wells uses it, in regard to the mind itself.

In scientific research, observation is not always direct; much use is made of instruments and apparatus. Instead of the eye, the photographic film or the photoelectric cell may be used. Sound vibrations may be measured electrically. Instruments have many advantages over the unaided senses. The microscope makes very small things visible. The telescope collects light from a large lens surface and then enables magnification to be applied. Moreover, such instrumental methods of observation enable us to overcome the limitations imposed by the recording system of the brain. It does not matter how unexpected or how rapid and transient a phenomenon is, if we have a photographic record of it. A motion picture of the disturbance in the classroom would have enabled all observers to agree on the facts after they had seen it several times. The sudden flash of the lines in the spectrum at the second contact point of an eclipse can be recorded photographically and studied at leisure.

Observations made with instruments are essentially judgments of coincidence. The observer measures a length by seeing the point at which the object to be measured comes

into coincidence with a mark on a scale, or weighs by observing the weight which will enable the pointer of the balance to swing uniformly over the center of the scale.   The
impersonal data, therefore, that form the basis of scientific
knowledge come from judgments of coincidence, and it is
only when such determinations of coincidence can be made
that general agreement between different observers is found.
When men are asked to judge the values of truth or beauty,
goodness or merit, there is no approximation to universal
agreement; but different observers will agree when they are
making coincidence observations.

It is true that the precision of coincidence observations is
limited.   A scientist is sometimes asked how he can tell that
certain points really coincide.   The answer is that the word
really has no meaning.   Within certain limits, fixed by the
sensitivity of the instrument and by the skill of the individual in judging coincidence, different observers will agree.
As Newton wrote in a letter in 1675, dispute about what can
be observed in an experiment "is to be decided not by dis-
course but by new trial of the experiment." *

In the observation of facts, the scientist and, indeed, all
human beings select some of the facts for attention and do
not treat all of them in the same way.   Scientific facts represent, indeed, only a very small portion, selected from all the
facts that could be observed.   The selection depends upon
the previous knowledge and upon the interest of the observer.
Suppose, of two men entering a room, one was extremely
thirsty, and the other was a painter interested in modern art.
The first on entering the room would see the jug of water on
the table, and, whether or not his manners would restrain
him from making a dash at it, the jug would certainly be
the center of his interest until his thirst was satisfied.   The
artist, not being thirsty, would probably not be conscious of
the existence of the jug.   His interest might be attracted by
a picture on the wall.   An extreme case of this difference in

* George, *op. cit.,* p. 100.

interest and experience is shown when an animal, a dog, for instance, enters a room in which people are sitting. The dog's reaction to his new environment is quite different from that of any human being.

The scientist in general, being by definition a person curious concerning facts and eager to record and arrange them, observes phenomena somewhat differently from other human beings. The parody addressed to Huxley * by Miss May Kendall comes to mind:

> Primroses by the river's brim
> Dicotyledons were to him,
> And they were nothing more.

But when scientists are definitely making observations in practical research, they go much further. They deliberately choose certain facts for observation, facts which in some way fit into the pattern in which they are interested. When a scientist has selected the facts which he wishes to observe and has made the necessary coincidence observations, for instance, by means of instruments, he classifies the facts. In biology, and especially the more general biological work which comes under the heading of natural history, classifications sometimes remain simple classifications; at any rate, for a long period. Thus Charles Darwin classified enormous numbers of facts relating to the properties and habits of animals of many kinds in all parts of the world. But, eventually, the scientist, if he is really a scientist, desires to cover this whole classification by some statement or formula into which the observations can be integrated as a whole. Darwin, who had collected great numbers of facts relating to the existence and survival of species among animals, finally evolved his doctrine of natural selection and embodied the whole in his great book, *On the Origin of Species*. It must always be remembered that it is the observed facts themselves that have validity, and the formulae or statements about

* Leonard Huxley, *Life and Letters of T. H. Huxley,* p. 112, Vol. I, London, Macmillan and Co., 1900.

them are merely convenient methods of summarizing them, classifying them, and suggesting the possibility of the observation of further facts. Facts are the foundation of science however they may be interpreted. As Faraday said:

> I cannot doubt but that he who, as a wise philosopher, has most power of penetrating the secrets of nature, and guessing by hypothesis . . . will also be most careful . . . to distinguish that knowledge which consists of assumption, by which I mean theory and hypothesis, from that which is the knowledge of facts and laws, never raising the former to the dignity or authority of the latter nor confusing the latter more than is inevitable with the former.*

The patterns into which scientific men fit the facts which they have observed are generally known as *hypotheses* or *theories*. In practice, a theory is an elaborate hypothesis that deals with a wider range of facts than does the simple hypothesis. In the initial stages, especially before verification, what is later called a theory is often called an hypothesis. At the point where an hypothesis is formed after the consideration of the observed facts, the scientist ceases to consider only the facts and proceeds to draw on his imagination. He attempts to see some connection between the facts he has observed, to form some pattern that he can generalize into which they fit. Then he examines his generalization to see whether any facts relevant to the subject and of the type which he has been observing invalidate that generalization. This is the very important verification of a theory; an unverified theory is merely an initial guess and is not accepted as valid. Further verification is obtained by deducing from the theory results leading to facts that can be tested by observation. If this test is met and the facts are established, the theory is considered to have strong support and to be a scientific theory having validity until facts are discovered that are not consonant with it. Thus we see that a scientific theory is formulated by the examination of a selected group

* Michael Faraday, *Philosophical Magazine,* **24,** 136 (1844). (Quoted by George.)

of facts in accordance with certain basic ideas that may be termed the *postulates*. It is necessary that these postulates should be logical and that they should be clear in the sense that they can be reasoned about. Moreover, in scientific work stress is laid on the simplicity of the postulates and on the postulates being as few in number as possible. The simplicity rule is always applied when a choice must be made between two theories. Newton says: "Nature is pleased with simplicity." * This is so well recognized in scientific work that there are classic statements of the rules of systematic inquiry. William of Occam, the English philosopher of the fourteenth century, expressed it in a phrase which is known as "Occam's razor." In Hamilton's translation, it is: "Neither more, nor more onerous causes are to be assumed than are necessary to account for the phenomena." Newton's version in his *Rules of Philosophizing* reads: "No more causes of natural things are to be admitted than such as are both true and sufficient to explain the phenomena of these things."

In practice, this demand for simplicity competes with the further requirements that the theory shall fit as many types of fact as possible. The very simple rule that Robert Boyle gave for the relation between the volume and the pressure of a gas holds for only a limited range of pressures. In order to cover a wider range, it must be complicated by the addition of the term suggested by van der Waals.

George points out that, provided the postulates of a theory are sound, it does not matter if they appear absurd or contrary to common sense. Almost everything new appears absurd. Absurdity is associated primarily with the unusual. The headdress of a Zulu rickshaw man does not appear absurd to a resident of Durban, but it would excite a great deal of interest and amusement in San Francisco. And the story of the ridicule excited by the first umbrella should warn us against regarding the appearance of absurdity as having any relation to value. Both the quantum theory of Planck and

* George, *op. cit.,* p. 240.

the relativity theory of Einstein appeared completely absurd when introduced. Ralph Fowler wrote in *Nature* in 1934, "Nothing could have exceeded the apparently wild extravagance of de Broglie's first work on electron waves which led directly to quantum mechanics." This does not mean that the formulator of a scientific theory would try to make his theory appear absurd or contrary to common sense. It means only that common sense has nothing whatever to do with scientific theorizing or with the practice of scientific research. Common sense is a judgment depending on common beliefs rather than logic. As Enriques says, "It is a prudent safeguard for whoever wants to spare himself the critical study of scientific expressions." *

In an analysis of the part played by theory in the development of science, Margenau † divides the world of the scientist into two parts: sense data and constructs. The sense data we have discussed as facts or coincidence data; the constructs are concepts invented by certain rules and bearing certain relations to sense data. We look at a line in the spectrum and say that it is blue. We associate this blueness with the existence of light and of light of a certain wave length. These ideas are *constructs*. Other constructs are, in mathematics, *number, integral, space;* in chemistry, *element, atom, compound, valence bond;* in physics, *electron, electric field, mass*. The ideas that form the body of scientific knowledge deal primarily with these constructs, which represent sense data symbolically and have properties that permit their discussion logically and with the aid of mathematics. These are a scientist's operations:

The scientist assembles his facts, he translates his data into constructs that he invents for the purpose according to certain rules that experience has shown to be useful. He then assembles these constructs, frequently using the language and

* Enriques, *Problems of Science,* English translation, p. 329, London, 1924. (Quoted by George, *op. cit.,* p. 247.)

† H. Margenau, "Theory and Scientific Development," *Scientific Monthly,* **LVII,** 63 (1943).

methods of mathematics, into a theory and, finally, he verifies the theory by deriving from it new conclusions that can be determined by observation. The evolution of the scientific method has depended upon the realization of the importance of these operations and, particularly, of the importance of verification before any theory is allowed to fit into the existing pattern of scientific knowledge.

When a set of scientific facts can be summarized by a simple statement and, especially, when that statement can be expressed in a mathematical form, it is said to be a *law*. Physical observations generally are classified by means of laws that can be expressed in mathematical form.

When a set of observations is finally reduced to a law or mathematical form, the scientist who succeeds in the effort feels a sense of satisfaction and receives the approval of his scientific colleagues, especially if the formula that he has developed covers a wide field of previously unreduced observations. Sometimes, on the other hand, new observations which would be expected to fit into a known formula do not do so. This raises questions as to whether the observations are erroneous, whether some factor has been ignored, or whether the formula is not broad enough to include the new observations. The discovery of facts that are fundamentally new and that require a considerable revision of established laws to represent them is an important event in the history of science and one that is frequently misunderstood, particularly by the layman.

In the nontechnical interpretations of science, whether written by laymen or by professional scientific workers, the nature of scientific theory and law is very rarely borne in mind and made clear to the reader. In any case it is difficult to make the layman understand the nature of a scientific law. This is partly perhaps because of the unfortunate name that has been given to it.* We speak of "laws" in various senses—

* The origin of the term is discussed by E. Zilsel in his article, "The Genesis of the Concept of Physical Law," *Philosophical Review*, **LI**, 245 (May 1942). He points out that the roots of this concept go back

the laws of men, which are enforced by police power; the laws of God, which are thought to be enforced by supernatural authority.

When a scientist speaks of a law, the public thinks that, if the law is disobeyed, some penalty will follow. But a scientific law is not an order which must be obeyed; it is a statement of fact. There is no way of obeying or disobeying it, and since disobedience is impossible, there is no penalty. The so-called laws of health can be disobeyed; they are statements of desirable action that have been formulated. But the law of gravity cannot be defied. If a man jumps out of a window and is caught in a net, he is not defying the law of gravity; he is acting according to the law of gravity.

The feeling that there is some connection between natural law and divine law has given rise to the idea that, in his establishment of *laws,* the scientist is approaching some form of absolute truth—that the whole process of scientific research, in fact, is the uncovering of truth and, if we only knew enough, we should be able to approach to a knowledge of absolute truth concerning all things. This idea leads to the personification of the existence of *nature,* an order of things external to ourselves concerning which generalizations may be made. Such a personification is often to be found in the writings of scientific men, especially those written for lay-

---

to antiquity. The divine lawgiver is the central idea of Judaism, and since God in addition is the creator of the world, it is easy to understand that the idea arose of his having prescribed certain prohibitions to the physical world. Thus Job says that God made a law for the rain. In classical antiquity also is to be found the idea that physical processes are enforced by gods.

The term *law* was used by Francis Bacon as synonymous with *form,* and Bacon probably derived the term from the Bible. Kepler used the word to some extent, and Descartes adopted the whole concept of natural law referring to the laws that God has put into nature, arguing, in fact, that natural laws must be immutable because God and his operations are perfect and immutable. The word in its present sense owes its popularity primarily to its adoption by Newton, who, however, used the term without any tinge of metaphysics and simply as the description of a phenomenon.

men. But *nature* is only the summation of observed facts fitted into patterns which resume and classify them.

The approach of a scientist to the phenomena which he observes may be realized perhaps by means of an analogy. Suppose you enter a room and see a man playing a violin. You say at once that this is a musical instrument and is producing sound. But suppose that the observer were absolutely deaf from birth, had no idea of hearing, and had never been told anything about sound or musical instruments, his whole knowledge of the world having been achieved through senses other than hearing. This deaf observer entering the room where a violinist was playing would be entirely unable to account for the phenomenon. He would see the movements of the player, the operation of the bow on the strings, the peculiarly shaped instrument, but the whole thing would appear to him irrational. But if he were a scientist interested in phenomena and in their classification, he would presently find that the movement of the bow on the violin produced vibrations, and these vibrations could be detected by means of physical instruments, and their wave form could be observed. After some time, it might occur to him that the vibrations of the strings and violin would be communicated to the air and could be observed as changes of pressure. Then he could record the changes of pressure produced in the air in the playing of a piece of music, and by analyzing the record could observe that the same groups of pressure changes were repeated periodically. Eventually he could attain to a knowledge of the whole phenomenon of music—the form of musical composition and the nature of different musical forms—but none of this would give him any approach to absolute truth in that he would still be unaware of the existence of sound as a sense and of the part that music could play in the mental life of those who could hear.

To the scientist as such, absolute reality has no meaning. It is a metaphysical conception, not a scientific one. The scientist neither affirms nor denies it; he merely ignores it. His purpose in forming abstract ideas is to classify facts observed through his senses, especially those facts that are observed by the methods of coincidences using instruments. And his interest in making this classification is greatly stimulated, perhaps chiefly stimulated, by the fact that from it he can deduce the possibilities of observing and correlating other facts.

It is impossible to discuss the method of the scientist without giving the impression that it is a purposeful method, that the scientist is aware of what he is doing, but this is usually not the case. A scientist does not always collect facts and deliberately endeavor to fit those facts into a pattern. He often collects the facts and continuously fits them into patterns without regard to the process itself. He may select the facts in which he is interested and attempt to fit them together into a theory, change his mind and try another theory, abandon some facts about which he is doubtful, and replace them by others without any conscious direction of the operation.* In this process, the scientist draws upon his imagination and relies upon his intuition. The operation, in fact, is largely performed by the subconscious mind, and it is in the facility with which they do this that scientists differ most in their quality.

In practical scientific discovery and in technology, three factors are involved, and people vary considerably in their ability as regards these individual factors. They are theoretical synthesis, observation and experiment, and invention. Psychologically, each involves distinct methods of working and different types of mind. There is even opposition among them; that is, it is unlikely that one man will excel in more

* Charles Singer (*A Short History of Science,* Oxford, Clarendon Press, 1941) points out that scientific articles, and especially scientific textbooks, give a false impression of the process by which investigators reach their conclusions. In articles and books, no information is given on the false starts and discarded hypotheses. The account reads as though the work ran smoothly to its inevitable conclusion in accordance with the principles of scientific investigation. As Singer says, "For this reason, among others, science can never be learned from books, but only by contact with phenomena."

than one direction. It is rare, for instance, for a capable inventor to be a theoretical thinker. Some scientists excel in their ability to visualize general syntheses and thus evolve theories. Some excel in their skill in observation or in their ingenuity in designing experiments. Some have a capacity for inventing and can design entirely new ways of accomplishing their ends. In addition, certain qualities that are not in any way connected with the scientific mind are, nevertheless, of great value in scientific work. In some fields of science, organizing ability is valuable, and men who are outstanding in one of the other factors will be specially qualified to use their organizing ability to promote the progress of science. Other qualities of considerable value are clarity of thought and ease of expression, and scientists differ as much in these attributes as do other men.

Scientists and technologists can advantageously be classified according to the extent to which they possess the three scientific factors and the ability to organize. Descartes, for instance, possessed a great power of theoretical synthesis. We have no evidence that he could experiment or that he showed any ability to invent. He probably had no opportunity for organization. Galileo was not only a good theorist but an excellent experimenter, and some of his work suggests that he had considerable ability as an inventor. Newton was outstanding in his capacity for theoretical understanding and as an experimenter. It is improbable that he had any considerable talent for invention in spite of his work on the telescope and on some other instruments.

Turning to the moderns, we may compare three great inventors: Lord Kelvin, Thomas Edison, and Elihu Thomson. Of these, Kelvin was a most capable theorist, an excellent experimenter, and an outstanding inventor. There is some reason to believe that he was lacking in capacity for organization, but his distinction in the other three fields makes him one of the greatest scientists of all time. Edison seems to have been purely an inventor. He was not interested in theory, and his experiments were conducted not to obtain knowledge but to make something work. He is, of course, *the* inventor *par excellence*. Thomson was far more of a scientist than Edison. He made a great number of inventions, and his excellent organizing ability gave him a rank in applied science that vies with that of Kelvin and Edison.

To a very great extent, the choice of the subject on which a scientist focuses his attention is a matter of fancy or even of chance. Moreover, not infrequently he does not succeed in reaching the end that he sought. Very often important discoveries are made by workers who are not looking for them, and great advances in science have arisen from a simple study of natural phenomena.

The great value of applied science has led to a school of thought that argues that scientific discovery is only justified by its application and that scientific research should, in fact, be engaged in only when it can be applied. This doctrine has been expressed very explicitly by some of the philosophers of the Soviet Union. It is endorsed also by such writers as Professor J. D. Bernal, who lays great stress upon the "frustration" of science, by which term he summarizes his belief that under a better (in his case, a collectivist) system of society, the development and, especially, the application of science would contribute more rapidly to the improvement of human welfare.* The fact is, however, that it is quite

* The origin of the feeling of frustration by experts such as Bernal is discussed by F. A. von Hayek (*The Road to Serfdom,* p. 53, University of Chicago Press, 1944). Von Hayek points out that "almost every one of the technical ideals of our experts could be realized within a comparatively short time if to achieve them were made the sole aim of humanity. There is an infinite number of good things, which we all agree are highly desirable as well as possible, but of which we cannot hope to achieve more than a few within our lifetime, or which we can hope to achieve only very imperfectly. It is the frustration of his ambitions in his own field that makes the specialist revolt against the existing order. We all find it difficult to bear to see things left undone that everybody must admit are both desirable and possible. That these things cannot all be done at the same time, that any one of them can be achieved only at the sacrifice of others, can be seen only by taking into account factors that fall outside any specialism."

impossible to predict in advance whether any particular scheme of scientific work will produce results which can be "applied." No one would have guessed that Lord Rayleigh's work on the density of nitrogen would have affected street lighting or that Gregor Mendel's study of peas would be of the utmost importance in the breeding of cattle; nor, in fact, was the applicability of these researches recognized for many years after they had been completed. All the arguments as to the applicability of scientific research are *ex post facto*. Moreover, it is the general opinion of those engaged in the application of science that there is no frustration in Professor Bernal's sense. Bernal believes that when the application of a scientific discovery can be seen to have been delayed, the delay should be ascribed to the faults and weaknesses of those who might have applied it. The practical men know that such delays are often due to conditions unknown to the critics and are unavoidable. Those who have themselves engaged in the slow and difficult task of translating a laboratory discovery into a product available to the public know how many pitfalls lie in the path. Our difficulty is not "frustration"; it is ignorance in each individual case. What is needed to solve the difficulty is not organization; it is more knowledge.

The creation of scientific knowledge, the advancement of science, has been carried out by the methods discussed in this chapter. The whole operation is so individualistic, it depends so much upon the psychology of the various scientific workers, that it is difficult if not impossible to direct it, even if a general agreement were possible as to the goal toward which it should be directed. Many times in the history of science the greatest experts have expressed themselves as to the feasibility of solving certain problems or achieving certain results, and in most cases their decisions have been erroneous. The application of science can be directed to produce results of value; the creation of science proceeds from the free operation of the minds of scientists.

The scientist, whether his work is the creation of knowledge without thought of its application or is the application of scientific knowledge to the use of mankind, may adopt as his motto and guide the words of Thomas Henry Huxley: *

> Thus, without for a moment pretending to despise the practical results of the improvement of natural knowledge, and its beneficial influence on material civilization, it must, I think, be admitted that the great ideas, some of which I have indicated, and the ethical spirit which I have endeavoured to sketch, in the few moments which remained at my disposal, constitute the real and permanent significance of natural knowledge.
>
> If these ideas be destined, as I believe they are, to be more and more firmly established as the world grows older; if that spirit be fated, as I believe it is, to extend itself into all departments of human thought, and to become co-extensive with the range of knowledge; if, as our race approaches its maturity, it discovers, as I believe it will, that there is but one kind of knowledge and but one method of acquiring it; then, we, who are still children, may justly feel it our highest duty to recognize the advisableness of improving natural knowledge, and so to aid ourselves and our successors in our course towards the noble goal which lies before mankind.

* Thomas Henry Huxley, "On the Methods and Results of Ethnology," *Collected Essays*, VII, London, Macmillan and Co., 1899.

Chapter IV

THE DEVELOPMENT OF THE
SCIENTIFIC METHOD

Having considered the nature of the scientific method, let us return to the course of human history and study the origin of that sudden change in the seventeenth century, from which came the developments in technology and science that have changed the life of man. We have seen that if we judge the level of civilization by its accomplishments and, particularly, by the arts of sculpture and architecture, of which the products·of many generations of men are available, it appears to move in cycles.

At the beginning of a cycle, the sculpture and architecture are primitive or, to use the more appropriate term, archaic. Gradually the artists improve in the freedom of their style until a point of high excellence is reached; then degeneration sets in, the style becomes overornate or formalized, and finally we are justified in speaking of decadence. Yet, while these cycles recur age after age, varying greatly in details and in the changes which are of importance in each cycle, there has been a definite progress in the knowledge and technical skill of men. This progress is due to the slow accumulation of technology and even slower accumulation of scientific knowledge. This slow growth, however, has accelerated greatly at certain historical periods. Perhaps the traditional account of the knowledge of Imhotep, vizier of Zoser, the outstanding king of the Third Dynasty of Ancient Egypt, is a memory of one of those periods. Imhotep was so greatly revered that he was deified as the patron god of learning and was eventually identified with Asklepios, the Greek god of medicine. As James Breasted says: "In priestly wisdom, in magic, in the formulation of wise proverbs, in medicine and architecture . . . he left so notable a reputation that his name was never forgotten." * As we shall see later, another period in which great progress was made in science followed the death of Alexander, in the third century B.C. In the sixteenth and seventeenth centuries, the growth of modern science began and has continued to accelerate to the present day.

The advance in wealth, comfort, and convenience that has characterized the last three hundred years has been achieved by a very small number of men, and even today our productive system is operated by a small group of men trained in the sciences who utilize the knowledge that has accumulated largely since the birth of Newton. This group is called "The Fifth Estate" by Dr. A. D. Little in an essay in which he discusses their relation to the rest of mankind.† He says:

> The fifth estate is composed of those who have the simplicity to wonder, the ability to question, the power to generalize, the capacity to apply. It is, in short, the company of thinkers, workers, expounders, and practitioners upon whom the world is absolutely dependent for the preservation and advancement of that organized knowledge which we call science.

Little considered that the effective number of those individuals was very small. In 1928, he guessed that there might be less than a hundred thousand in the world.

The history of the development of science is the history of the evolution of this small body of specialized workers, who originally took an interest in science as amateurs—those who loved the subject—and only in recent times became professionals devoting their whole time to study and the advancement of knowledge.

* James Breasted, *A History of Egypt,* p. 112, New York, Charles Scribner's Sons, 1912.

† A. D. Little, *The Handwriting on the Wall,* p. 253, Boston, Little, Brown and Co. and Atlantic Monthly Press, 1928.

The growth of scientific knowledge started so suddenly at the beginning of the seventeenth century that it might almost be considered a revolution. As we study the course of this revolution, it becomes evident that it represents a unique event in history, and it is difficult to understand why it did not occur earlier. We can, of course, ascribe the rapid growth of science in the seventeenth century to the existence of certain men, Galileo, Boyle, and Newton, for example, but such individuals are known through all the ages of history. Why did not the Greeks develop experimental science? Singer says: "By the end of the fifth century B.C., not only had philosophical thought taken a scientific turn, but science itself had emerged as a preoccupation of men set aside from their fellows." * Later many of the Hellenistic Greeks of the Alexandrian school—Archimedes, for instance—were famous for their interest in natural philosophy and for the inventions that they made. But, in spite of the progress for which they themselves were responsible, they did not act as catalysts to set off a sudden growth of science contributed to by many other men.

Several explanations are possible for the unique phenomena of the seventeenth century. Zilsel studied the emergence of modern science as a sociological process.† He points out that the end of the Middle Ages was a period of rapidly progressing technology and of technological inventions and that in the fifteenth century economic competition and the spirit of enterprise were emerging from the fetters of the feudal system. Feudal society was ruled by tradition and custom, whereas the early capitalism proceeded rationally. It calculated and measured, introduced bookkeeping, and began to use machines. Thus at this period the social ban against personal labor weakened sufficiently to enable educated men to carry out experiments with their own hands.

* Charles Singer, *A Short History of Science,* p. 30, Oxford, Clarendon Press, 1941.

† E. Zilsel, "Sociological Roots of Science," *The American Journal of Sociology,* **XLVII**, 544 (1942).

In the ancient world, the craftsmen were slaves, and it was below the dignity of a man of the upper class to handle materials himself. One profession in Greece was partially exempt from this rule, that of medicine. A genuine experimental science in medicine and especially in surgery, diet, and gymnastics was developed by the Greeks. It was embodied in the writings attributed to Hippocrates of Cos, in which are described the clinical observations of patients suffering from various diseases. The followers of Hippocrates had the correct scientific method, but the development of science in medicine was impossible at that time. The true science of medicine depends upon the advance of physiology, and the physiology of the human body is so complex that medicine is still largely empirical.

Instead of developing experimental science, the most popular Greek philosophers based their views of nature on *a priori* assumptions,* and their progress was largely confined to pure mathematics, especially geometry and the theory of numbers. Their actual progress in physics was certainly much handicapped by their feeling that practical experimental work was not suitable for a philosopher and thinker. If this seems strange, we should remember that the feeling existed in some English universities not more than fifty years ago. Charles L. Dodgson, better known as Lewis Carroll, wrote a most violent diatribe against the supply of funds for scientific research at Oxford.†

The social ban on the practical handling of materials probably did not exist in Egypt, where the rulers not infrequently boast in their tombs of their accomplishments as engineers and where some of the priests were noted for their knowledge

---

* Nevertheless, Thales, the first outstanding Greek scientist, enunciated the fundamental scientific principle of the sequence of cause and effect. It was largely the influence of the Pythagoreans and of Plato that diverted the Greek mind from observational and experimental science.

† *Fame's Penny Trumpet,* 1876, and also letter to *Pall Mall Gazette,* "Natural Science at Oxford," *Life and Letters of Lewis Carroll,* by S. P. Collingwood, p. 187, London, Fisher Unwin, 1898.

of medicine. But many technical developments in Egypt reached a certain level and then ceased to progress, so that it is not astonishing that experimental science did not develop to a greater degree in the Egyptian system.

There is yet another possible explanation for the failure of the ancient world to discover the method of experimental science. The individual scientist, however much he might discover personally, had no satisfactory way of communicating it to his fellows before the art of printing was discovered. He could, of course, write manuscripts, but he had no means of knowing all those to whom his manuscripts would be of interest; and it must be remembered that experimental science, especially in earlier times, was of interest only to a very small audience. The specialists today from whom the great advances come have an understanding audience of only a few people in the whole world. The rest do not read original papers or, if they do read them, do not realize what has been done. Realization and acceptance by the scientific world as a whole await recognition by the specialists and the explanation of the work by other writers than the original discoverers. Moreover, interest and ability in writing are not necessarily correlated with interest and ability in experimental discovery. Newton communicated his results to the Royal Society in the most casual manner; and, if it had not been for the insistence of Edmund Halley, it is doubtful if Newton's collected papers would ever have been published in such a form that they could produce the effect achieved by the publication of the *Principia*.

In the earlier days, there was no mechanism whatever by which the scientist could find an audience. Nor was he often interested in finding an audience. The poet, the dramatist, and even the eloquent speaker might write for the delight and interest of his fellow men; the philosopher and teacher would write; but the experimental scientist would make his observations, store them in his memory, tell a few of his friends, whose attitude toward him might be one either of derision or of uncomprehending veneration, and the knowledge he had won would generally die with him. But after the invention of printing, scientific works could be reproduced so easily that they had a much larger circulation and, thus, a much greater chance of reaching the few students of the subject. The great book of Copernicus, for instance, published when he was on his deathbed, produced an impression on all astronomers.

The early history of science is only slowly emerging through the work of the archaeologists. As in other fields in the history of human understanding, there is little doubt but that, as we learn more of the ancient world, we shall find that that world knew more than we realize of the ideas that we value today. The Dawn of Conscience, which fifty years ago would have been ascribed to the early Hebrew prophets, whose work we happen to have in written form dating from the eighth century b.c., has now been traced by Breasted back beyond the Old Kingdom of Egypt to a period as remote from that of Amos as Amos is from us. And so it is not unlikely that many of the scientific ideas that we meet first among the Greeks had their true origin in Babylon or in Egypt or even perhaps in Crete or the Hittite Empire. We simply do not know the origin of many of the ideas that the Greeks developed in systematic and written form. Much valuable work has been done recently on the mathematical and astronomical ideas of the Babylonians and on the methods used by the Egyptian engineers, but it is not until we reach the beginning of the classic era in Greece that we meet an organized school of science.

The philosopher to whom the Greeks ascribed the earliest scientific thought was Thales of Miletus, who achieved fame by his prophecy of the eclipse of 585 b.c., a prophecy which he was able to make from information on the timing of eclipses that he had acquired during a visit to Babylon. Thales worked chiefly on geometry. His pupil Anaximander was interested in geography and the making of maps. Heraclitus of Ephesus, Leucippus of Miletus, and Democritus advocated *a priori* views of the "nature of things," and Pythag-

oras of Samos gave the philosophy of science a mystical turn
that took it far from the path to which it had been directed
by Thales and Hippocrates. Then the whole trend of Greek
thought was revolutionized by the teaching of Socrates. In
his youth, Socrates studied physics, and it is interesting to
speculate as to what would have happened if he had continued to be interested in science. But Socrates grew im-
patient with the difficulty he found in deducing science from
a single fundamental idea, and turned instead to the teaching
that it is the great business of life to practice the care of one's
own soul. Socrates followed Pythagoras in believing that
reality consists of abstract ideas and that mathematical truths
were divine and illustrated the nature of the mind of God, a
view that has been advocated to some extent by modern
mathematicians. Thus Socrates and Plato, his great follower,
rejected experimental science and established the priority of
mind over matter.

The outstanding philosopher through whom the views of
the ancient Greeks were made available to a later world was
Aristotle, who seems to have combined the power of an original and creative thinker with the instincts of a natural
teacher. Aristotle at the age of seventeen left Macedon for
Athens to study under Plato. He worked on mathematics
and physics and wrote treatises on astronomy and physics.
In these fields he followed the platonic philosophy and deduced the laws of nature from *a priori* assumptions, at the
same time adopting the conclusions of the Pythagoreans, who
used arithmetic relations as the basis of the physical world.
Thus he adopted the idea of Empedocles of Acragas in Sicily,
that matter is composed of four elements, each of which is
distinguished by two primary qualities: fire is hot and dry;
air, hot and fluid; water, cold and fluid; and earth, cold and
dry. After the death of Plato, Aristotle began more and
more to abandon these *a priori* assumptions and to rely on
observation. Perhaps because he was the son of a physician,
he turned to the field of biology, in which he made very rapid
progress. The material that Aristotle wrote on biology is in

startling contrast to that which he wrote on physics. In his discussion of one set of observations, we might hear Bacon or Newton writing two thousand years later: ". . . the facts have not yet been sufficiently grasped; if they ever are, then credit must be given to observations rather than to theories and to theories only in so far as they are confirmed by the observed facts."

Aristotle was the tutor of Alexander the Great. After the death of Alexander in 323 B.C., his general, Ptolemy, became king of Egypt and established his capital at Alexandria. In Alexandria, Ptolemy II founded the Museum, in which the personal schools of Plato and Aristotle were developed into a university. And there arose the greatest school of the ancient world, in which most of the best scientists of the time were professors. At the Museum, Euclid established his system of geometry, which became the standard of the world for more than two thousand years; Aristarchus was the leading astronomer; Archimedes, the outstanding mathematician and physicist. Archimedes himself came from Syracuse, to which he returned after his studies in Alexandria. Eratosthenes made such precise observations in astronomy that he was able to calculate the diameter of the earth with considerable accuracy and to elucidate the necessity for the Julian calendar, with its Leap Year. An even more accurate observer was Hipparchus, who discovered the precession of the equinoxes and established theoretical astronomy in the form that it retained until the time of Copernicus. The civilization of Alexandria was, however, doomed to collapse. The history of the Ptolemies is one of steadily worsening government until finally the Romans absorbed the fragments of the Alexandrine Empire.

The prevalent philosophy among the Roman leaders was Stoicism, which laid great stress on conduct and duty and had a completely rigid conception of nature. The Epicurean philosophy was less widely adopted but had greater influence on those few Romans who were interested in science or in the writing of philosophy. Of these, by far the best known is Lucretius, whose book, *On the Nature of Things,* is often regarded as a predecessor of our modern ideas, especially as Lucretius, following the Epicurean philosophy, explains the origin of the entire world as due to the interaction of atoms, so that atoms are the only reality. The best-known writer on scientific subjects during the Roman period was the elder Pliny, who wrote a natural history consisting of a vast collection of observations and statements about animals and plants, many of them hearsay. Pliny's book formed a kind of encyclopedia that was accepted as the best description of the natural world for a thousand years; and, although undoubtedly it represented progress at the time, its authority was eventually detrimental to the improvement of natural knowledge.

More and more, the Greek inspiration, which so nearly achieved the discovery of the experimental method of science, died out, and, except for the occasional appearance of individual thinkers, the world steadily receded into intellectual darkness. Among these individual thinkers, one of the greatest was Galen of Pergamum, who ranks with Hippocrates as the outstanding medical authority of the ancients. Galen made accurate anatomical and physiological studies of many animals and worked out a complete physiological system that survived as the accepted description of physiology until the sixteenth century. As Singer says, "The whole knowledge possessed by the world in the department of physiology— nearly all the biological conceptions, most of the anatomy, much of the botany, and all the ideas of the physical structure of living things from the third to the sixteenth century—were contained in a small number of works of Galen." *   The works were translated into many languages, commented on by later writers, and reproduced in many forms. Galen believed that everything was made by God to a particular end, a doctrine known as *teleology.* Because this view fitted the theological attitude of the Middle Ages so perfectly, Galen became the authority in his field.

* Charles Singer, *op. cit.,* p. 92.

The final blow to the study of science came from the development of Neoplatonism in Alexandria. This philosophy derived mainly from Plato, but in part also from Stoicism. In it, matter was considered to be governed by the Platonic "Idea" as the soul governs the body, and the factual study of science disappeared into mysticism. Neoplatonism lasted only about a century, but it passed into Christianity largely through the work of St. Augustine. With the coming of Christianity both the classical science and the classical philosophy vanished, and men devoted their intellects to the study of theology. Through this period there survived a memory of the writings of Aristotle, whose alleged views on the structure of the universe formed the framework on which the whole of medieval science came to be built. It was held that Aristotle felt that the stars were noble beings and exercised influence over the human destinies—a more definite and systematized astrology than that of the ancients; that the circle was a perfect geometrical figure; and that the stars, therefore, must move regularly in circles. Thus arose the doctrine of determinism, every man's life being assumed to be written at the time of his birth, a determinism that reached its most extreme development in the theological field with John Calvin.

This whole era filled one of the periods of great depression in the cycles of civilization. It followed the long decay of the Roman Empire, and for a time the world lay almost prostrate, ruined economically by the internecine struggles of the feudal system and lost spiritually in the squabbles of the monks, who, in the monasteries, carried on the only intellectual life. Francis Bacon said of the inhabitants of these monasteries:

Having sharp and strong wits, and abundance of leisure, and small variety of reading, but their wits being shut up in the cells of a few authors [chiefly Aristotle, their dictator], as their persons were shut up in the cells of monasteries and colleges, and knowing little history, either of nature or time, [they] did out of no great quantity of matter and infinite agitation of wit spin out unto us those laborious webs of learning which are extant in their books.

The Christian religion, which so greatly modified the message of the Greek thinkers as it was transmitted by the medieval scholars, was of Hebrew origin and was dominated by a doctrine that had no echo in Greek thought, the doctrine of authority. The account of cosmology, history, anthropology, religion, and ethics given in the Hebrew scriptures, together with the New Testament, was accepted as the unquestioned authority for all thought in that field, so that very soon opinion as to any event was based entirely upon what could be found on the subject in the Holy Scriptures or, if there was nothing available in the Scriptures, in the writings of the fathers, among whom Aristotle was often included. One may guess that Aristotle would have been very much astonished at the company in which he found himself.

At the universities, theology and scholasticism predominated even while the towns were emerging from the intellectual deadlock. Casuistry and fine-drawn distinctions became a game to which men devoted their lives, and natural phenomena were judged primarily for their theological implications. It was held always that each individual phenomenon had been decided by the will of God for a definite purpose and that the interest of man lay in detecting the purpose behind the will. Zilsel * says that the first representatives of secular learning appeared in the fourteenth century in Italian cities. They were the secretaries and officials of the governors of the cities who chiefly had to conduct the correspondence and external relations of their employers. To do this, they strove after perfection of style and the exhibition of knowledge, making their writings very polished and their speeches most eloquent. Thus the humanists emerged, who soon, because of their learning, became teachers—instructors of their employers' children and then professors at the universities. In this way, the humanist scholars became

* *Op. cit.*, p. 549.

part of the university system, and they were proud of their social rank and their education. They encouraged particularly the study of the ancient languages, in which the writings of the past were to be found. Curiously enough, much of Greek thought, the writings of Aristotle, for instance, had been kept alive during the Dark Ages of Europe by translation into Arabic and by preservation by the Arabs, who had swept over Africa and through a great part of Spain. No true eclipse of learning had occurred among the Arabs, whose cycle of civilization was in a different phase from that of the western world. But the Arabic philosophy, and particularly its devotion to the writings of the Prophet as the source of authority, provided little stimulus to original thinking. The writings of many of the Greek authors had been translated into Arabic through Syriac, which was the language in many parts of the Byzantine Empire and had from the third century replaced Greek in Western Asia. Thus, during the greatest period of Moslem rule in the eighth century, the old Syriac versions of the works of the outstanding Greek writers were revised, and in the next century many of them were translated into Arabic. Galen's writings as well as those of Aristotle were widespread in Arabic translations.

In the fourteenth century, the ancient classics began to be recovered, Greek was studied, and the Arabic works were translated into Latin and even retranslated into Greek. It was not until the fifteenth century that the original Greek versions were available instead of those that had passed through the difficulties of the Arabic translation. As has already been mentioned, the introduction of the art of printing in the middle of the fifteenth century was of the utmost importance for its influence on science. The first books to be printed were, however, the classics rather than the products of contemporary thought. First came the Bible and the works of authors of theological authority, then the treatises on law and medicine, and the writings of classical antiquity. Many contemporary writers are, however, to be found among the early printed books.

In the fifteenth century, feudalism began to collapse and to be replaced by capitalism. As Zilsel points out, in feudal society the castles of knights and rural monasteries were the centers of culture. In early capitalism culture was centered in ·the towns. This capitalism depended on the spirit of enterprise of the individual, whereas in medieval society the individual was dominated by the traditions of the group to which he belonged. With the individualism of the new society came the beginnings of invention and of scientific thinking.

In the sixteenth century, the "shaking of the dry bones" * became much more evident; and, in one field of science after another, individuals arose who departed from the traditions of the ancients and began to create knowledge themselves. Of these, by far the most gifted and original was Leonardo da Vinci, one of those men of great genius who illuminate an era. Leonardo was primarily a painter; although his artistic work was recognized as of the first rank, his greatest interest seems to have been in mechanical invention. He was the engineer for several princes of the time, but very little of his work seems to have been adopted. The fact is that Leonardo, like many inventors, had the primary ideas for very many more inventions than he could develop. Even today it would be difficult for one man, unless he were a great organizer, to develop to practical success the large number of inventions sketched in Leonardo's notebooks. A more practical, though far less gifted, man was Agricola, who wrote a great work on metals, in which he set forth the whole technology of mining.

In the field of biological knowledge, the first necessary step was to get rid of the idea that the ancient writings of Aristotle and Galen were authoritative. In the sixteenth century a man arose who set himself against the whole weight of authority. Born in Brussels in the second decade, Andreas Vesalius carried out his investigations on the anatomy of the

* *Ezekiel,* XXXVII.

human body, mainly in Italy. He soon found errors in Galen's descriptions and corrected them. Despite bitter opposition, Vesalius at last prevailed; and modern anatomy was born. Even more revolutionary in its opposition to authority than the work of Vesalius was that of Copernicus, which affected the whole thought of man with its new picture of the universe. This picture was important not only in its scientific aspect but also from the philosophical point of view. Before Copernicus, the earth was the center of the universe, and the teleological point of view, that the earth was created for man, was a basic idea of both philosophy and theology. With the abandonment of the earth as the center and the understanding that the sun was the center of the solar system, around which the planets revolved, man lost his intrinsic importance as the being around whom the whole universe was designed.

About this time, two great optical instruments were invented, the compound microscope and the telescope. The use of the telescope by Galileo led to his astronomical discoveries. In addition, Galileo throughout his life was occupied with physical investigations. His work opened the way to the advancement of the science of mechanics, especially because he was able to demonstrate experimentally the incorrectness of one of Aristotle's definite statements. Aristotle had stated that bodies should fall with velocities proportional to their weights. Galileo showed by direct experiment that this statement is incorrect. The effect of Galileo's experiment was much greater than the mere demonstration of a new fact might be assumed to be, because it tended to destroy the authority of Aristotle and to teach men that the validity of a fact is to be tested by direct experiment instead of by quotation of any authority, however great.

The first astronomical observation made by Galileo involved another disproof of an Aristotelian doctrine. In 1604, he observed a nova and found that, like the stars in general, it showed no parallax. Aristotle had regarded the outer zone of the stars as absolutely changeless, whereas the inner zones of the sun and planets showed changes. Yet here was a change in the stellar realm! In 1610, Galileo embodied the early astronomical discoveries that resulted from the use of the telescope in a little pamphlet, *The Messenger of the Heavens.* In it, he described the mountains of the moon, the great increase in the number of visible stars, and, above all, the satellites of Jupiter, which offered a model for the solar system as conceived by Copernicus. These and other observations produced an attack on Galileo, especially because much controversy arose as to the habitability of the moon, the planets, and even the stars. The idea of a plurality of inhabited worlds was felt to be contrary to the Christian doctrines as well as to those of Aristotle. The Inquisition ordered Galileo to abandon his opinions and to stop discussing them.

Galileo turned to the philosophy of science and discussed the properties of objects that are primary to the object and those that depend upon the observer and are secondary to the object. In this, we see the beginning of a definition of the special field of science, the subject of our third chapter. Then Galileo returned to his astronomical work and wrote his Dialogue between the Ptolemaic and Copernican systems, in which he endorsed the latter. It was received with enthusiasm by the learned but with wrath by the Inquisition, whose edict it clearly infringed. Galileo was arrested, forced to recant, and after a short period of imprisonment ordered to spend the remainder of his life in seclusion, a retirement that he used to the greatest advantage by further discoveries in mechanics and astronomy. By the time that Galileo died, in 1642, science had emerged from the medieval world, and the great revolution in the thought of man was under way.

Promoting this revolution also were two philosophers who did not themselves carry out any important experimental work. They were René Descartes and Francis Bacon.

Descartes believed that the laws of the universe could be deduced from certain simple and definite principles and that these principles apply to all phenomena everywhere. The aim of science, therefore, is to understand and define these basic principles; they can then be applied to any special case that is under investigation. Descartes believed that the correct principles could be selected by using their *clarity* as a criterion; the clearest image would be the most nearly correct. These ideas, which were similar to those of Pythagoras and his followers, represent an extension to other studies of the methods of mathematics, in which Descartes himself made great advances, applying algebraic methods to geometrical problems. The method of Descartes consisted in beginning with the simplest and surest notions and proceeding cautiously to deduce inferences. Descartes realized, of course, that knowledge is derived from experience as well as from deduction. In contrast to Bacon, however, he put more faith in deduction than in experience. Descartes' views on the philosophy of science represented a very wide break from the scholastic principles identified with the name of Aristotle; but they were of a form acceptable to the orthodox scholars of his time, and they received wide recognition.

Francis Bacon was a very extraordinary man. Born in 1561, the younger son of a British nobleman, he entered Trinity College, Cambridge, and at the age of eighteen took up residence at Gray's Inn and became a lawyer. His patron was the Earl of Essex, and Bacon's career was largely influenced by that of Essex. When Essex was tried on a charge of treason, Bacon was one of the Crown counsel, a fact that gave rise to much criticism. It was not until the accession of James I to the throne that Bacon had any chance of advancement. Then he was promoted rapidly until, in 1618, he was made Lord Chancellor. In 1621, however, his enemies discovered that he had been guilty of corrupt dealings, for which he was sentenced to a severe penalty, largely remitted by the king.*

The greater part of Bacon's important writings were published in the last five years of his life. Bacon was not a

---

* Compare John R. Baker, *The Scientific Life,* p. 52, London, George Allen & Unwin, Ltd., 1942.

scientist; he took no part in experimental work, and he was largely ignorant of the great work of the scientists of his time. Leonardo da Vinci in mechanics, Kepler in astronomy, Gilbert in electricity, and Vesalius in anatomy had made great contributions to scientific knowledge, but Bacon ignored all of them in his writing. He was a philosopher but, above all, he was a writer and advocate. He had a wonderful gift in his trenchant pen and in his facility of expression, and he carried the popular imagination with him in his emphasis on observation and experiment as against the acceptance of tradition. Bacon believed that all fruitful knowledge was to be based upon inference from particular occasions in the past to particular occasions in the future, and this he called the method of *inductive* reasoning. In addition, he had two ideas of the utmost importance, ideas that were instrumental in producing the scientific revolution. They were that knowledge is to be acquired primarily by observation and experiment and that the application of scientific knowledge could lead to practical results of the utmost value. Bacon overestimated the ease with which scientific knowledge can be obtained, and he fell into an error in which he is followed by many today—the error of believing that scientific research can be organized like an engineering project and that the way to make scientific discoveries is to plan to make them.

Bacon's first aim was to organize a system for the investigation of nature by observation and experiment. A great number of observed facts would be collected, and from them the fundamental processes of nature could be understood. In this way, he believed, it was possible to attain to "the knowledge of Causes and secret motions of things, and the enlarging of the bounds of Human Empire, to the effecting of all things possible." This was a great vision, a new vision on the earth, and a vision that has been realized. The method that Bacon suggested for carrying out this idea was the organization of a research institute,* which he entitled the "House

* Chapter VIII, p. 180.

of Salomon" and described in his *New Atlantis*. This institute contained a series of laboratories for experimental research equipped with Utopian perfection—caves in the ground, high towers, buildings on mountains, "the highest of them three miles at least; great lakes, both salt and fresh," pools, rocks in the sea, and bays upon the shore; artificial wells and fountains; great and spacious houses, in which could be imitated meteors and snow, hail, and rain; orchards and gardens full of trees and herbs, with soil of various kinds in which could be produced new plants differing from those known.

In these experimental stations and laboratories, Bacon saw the possibilities of experiments in genetics, physiology, pharmacology, mechanical arts, metallurgy, optics, crystallography, and all branches of physics and chemistry. This research institute was to be manned by a great company of Fellows, to whom Bacon, with his passion for detailed organization, allotted specific functions. Some were to study written works and to travel in search of knowledge from abroad; some were to make observations and experiments; and some were to carry out computations on the results of these experiments and to develop theories and devise new experiments. A noble dream, much before its time and greatly overorganized, but it led to the idea of co-operation in the pursuit of knowledge. From it came the impulse that founded the Royal Society. Martha Ornstein says that Bacon's description of the House of Salomon "bears to the cause of learned societies the same relation as does Marx's 'Communist Manifesto' to socialist propaganda. No historical account can ever be given of gatherings of learned societies without reference to this, their 'romantick' prototype." *

Bacon, however, was not really describing a learned society; he was describing a research institute or, rather, a group of research institutes. His plan was much more akin

* Martha Ornstein, *The Role of Scientific Societies in the Seventeenth Century,* p. 43, Chicago, University of Chicago Press, Third Edition, 1938.

to the Kaiser Wilhelm Institut or to the research institutes of the U.S.S.R. than to the Royal Society or the Académie des Sciences. In addition, Bacon believed, as some do today, that scientific research should be planned with a view to the application of discoveries to practical human needs. This has already been discussed,* but in any case it had no immediate effect upon the course of events. The discovery of the telescope and the microscope and the discussion of the wonders they revealed created widespread interest, and men from many strata of society joined the ranks of the amateurs studying new experiments. Many of these amateurs belonged to the English aristocracy, foremost among whom was Robert Boyle, a younger son of the great Earl of Cork. Boyle devoted his whole life to scientific research and discovered the relation between the pressure and the volume of a gas, still known as Boyle's law. When a young man, Boyle associated with a group of enthusiastic experimenters, to which he refers in a letter as "our invisible college." The meetings of this group were greatly interrupted by the Civil War, and it was not until the restoration of the monarchy that life in London could move on the old lines. But in 1660 a movement was made toward a definite organization of this interest in experimental philosophy, and in the next two years a society was formed that in 1662 was incorporated under the patronage of King Charles II with the name of the Royal Society.

Among those who founded the society were Robert Boyle, John Evelyn, and Sir Christopher Wren, who, though commonly thought of only as an eminent architect, was the most widely accomplished man of his time. Among the subjects in which he was a recognized authority were mathematics, astronomy, meteorology, and anatomy.

With the formation of the Royal Society, organization entered the history of science. For the first time, there were a nucleus and a meeting place for those interested in experi-

* Chapter III, p. 62.

mental science, a method of exchanging views, and, what was perhaps even more important, a method of publication. The first task of the Royal Society was to begin publication of its *Philosophical Transactions,* which has continued ever since.

In 1642 was born the greatest scientist of all time, Isaac Newton. It was expected that Newton would follow the farmer's life that had been led by his ancestors, but, when he was sixteen, he showed such incompetence as a farmer that he was sent back to school and thence to Cambridge. In 1665 the plague drove him from Cambridge, and in his mother's farmhouse the young man worked out his discoveries of the binomial theorem, the mathematics of infinite series, the differential and integral calculus, the idea of universal gravitation, the production of the spectrum by dispersion, and the formulation of the laws of mechanics, following the work of Galileo. In order to understand Newton's life, we must realize the difference between the attitude of the men of the seventeenth century toward their scientific work and that of the professional scientists of today. The founders of the Royal Society were, as has already been said, amateurs. They were experimenting and speculating in natural philosophy for their own interest. They considered their conclusions and their discoveries to be their own property, with which they could do as they pleased. As Sir James Jeans says, "We see Newton's terrifically powerful mind playing with the problems of science as we play with a crossword puzzle and regard the incident as finished when we have solved it." *

Newton discovered the calculus in 1665, yet, before publishing it even partially, he allowed twenty-eight years to elapse, years in which Gottfried von Leibniz discovered and published the same thing in Germany. At the same time, he satisfied himself that the force of gravity, obeying an inverse square law, explained the motion of the moon "pretty nearly" and was content to leave it at that until Halley asked him many years afterward what were the orbits of the planets.

---

* Sir James Jeans, "Newton and the Science of Today," *Nature,* 150, 712 (1942).

In reply, Newton casually remarked that he had solved the problem five years previously but had mislaid the proof. But for Halley's coaxing and insistence, Newton's great work would probably never have been published as a whole, and it owed its publication largely to a quarrel with Hooke and the sequel to that quarrel. The story of this extraordinary man in relation to the science of his age is discussed in an interesting series of papers published in *Nature* in 1942 to celebrate the tercentenary of his birth.

The Royal Society was not the first scientific society. That honor belongs to Italy, where the Accademia del Cimento (the Experimental Society) was organized in Florence in 1657. It was not an association of independent workers; it was formed by the Medici brothers—the Grand Duke Ferdinand II and Leopold of Tuscany. The Academy held its meetings at the palace of Leopold, who defrayed all expenses and was the active leader of the group. The members were ardent amateurs in experimental work, many of them disciples of Galileo or students of his disciples. When Leopold became a cardinal in 1667, the Academy was given up, but an account of the work of its members was published, entitled "Saggi di Naturali Esperienze Fatte Nell' Accademia del Cimento." This account contained so much experimental detail that it became the laboratory manual of the period. It was translated into English in 1684, Latin in 1731, French in 1755, and was republished in a new edition in 1780. This book formed the beginning of experimental physics and gave Italy the leadership in that field at the time.

The Académie des Sciences, founded in 1666, arose, like the Royal Society, from the meetings of a group of enthusiastic amateurs. Jean Baptiste Colbert, the great minister of Louis XIV, obtained for it the patronage of that monarch and the support of the French treasury. Colbert believed firmly in a strongly centralized government, a policy that was to some extent responsible for the misgovernment that eventually led to the French Revolution. The Académie was organized as a co-operative laboratory for scientific research rather than as a free association of scientific workers. The results of this co-operative work were of some value but, as a whole, the method proved a failure, and the most important discoveries were made by individuals. The most distinguished physicist, Huygens, was so dissatisfied that he withdrew.

In comparing the Académie with the Royal Society, we must remember that it had no member whose influence could rival Newton's, for which reason its work was of the greatest value toward the end of the eighteenth century, whereas the Royal Society had become world-famous a century earlier. The Berlin Academy was founded by Gottfried Wilhelm von Leibniz, whose life span was approximately contemporaneous with Newton's. Leibniz was, above all, a mathematician. His work covered the whole field of physics, however, and, in addition, he was determined to effect a reform of the educational system, especially that of the universities. He believed in the teaching of science and of "modern" subjects such as history, geography, and mathematics, and was strongly opposed to the emphasis placed on Latin, which acted as a barrier to the extension of education to the people. Leibniz made a series of proposals for the organization of a scientific society in Germany and finally seized an opportunity created by the formation of a commission to adopt the Catholic calendar. Leibniz proposed that the Elector of Brandenburg (the ruler of Prussia) should keep the monopoly of calendars and use the receipts to establish a learned society and an observatory. In 1700 the charter of the Berlin Academy was granted, with Leibniz as its president. The results, however, were disappointing, and Leibniz continued to agitate for the formation of other societies in Dresden, St. Petersburg, and Vienna.

The American Philosophical Society, the oldest scientific society in the United States, was founded by Benjamin Franklin in 1743 as the successor to a small group of enthusiasts, the "Junto," which dated from 1727. In 1769 the American Philosophical Society and the American Society joined to form the American Philosophical Society Held at Philadelphia for Promoting Useful Knowledge, under which name the society still flourishes.

The development of science in the seventeenth century and, indeed, in much of the eighteenth, was the work of the scientific societies rather than of the universities. These societies assumed responsibility for the progress of science and developed the experimental method, which found no welcome in the universities of that period, steeped as they were in the spirit of tradition. As Martha Ornstein says:

> It was the unmistakable and magnificent achievement of the scientific societies of the seventeenth century, not only to put modern science on a solid foundation, but in good time to revolutionize the ideals and methods of the universities and render them the friends and promoters of experimental science instead of the stubborn foes they had so long been.*

* Martha Ornstein, *op. cit.,* p. 263.

Chapter V

THE GROWTH OF PHYSICAL IDEAS

The science of physics originated in the study of the movements of the heavenly bodies. The apparent movements of the sun and moon in relation to the earth and the movement of the planets through the constellations of the stars, the annual rise and fall of the altitude of the sun, were obviously related to the seasons and, therefore, to agriculture, to seed time and harvest, and to such phenomena as the inundation of the Nile, upon which the existence of Egypt depended. After the first fanciful images, the traverse of the heavens by the sun in a boat, for instance, a very definite cosmology was developed to account for the observed facts; and this system became more and more complicated as the accuracy of the observations increased. The practical requirements of engineering also demanded a system of mensuration, which involved methods of determining the volumes of spheres, cylinders, pyramids, and the areas of conic sections. The early methods available to the astronomers and engineers were essentially geometrical in form, and geometry continued as the principal mathematical discipline until the eighteenth century, when it was largely replaced by algebra.

It was in physical science that the Alexandrian school of philosophers approached the discovery of the method of experimental science; * and it was, again, in physical science that Galileo initiated the scientific revolution.†   Galileo's experiments showed that the acceleration of falling bodies is not proportional to their weight, as was believed by the followers of Aristotle, but that light and heavy bodies fall

* Chapter IV, p. 72.
† Chapter IV, p. 78.

in the same time and, therefore, with the same acceleration. This discovery marks the beginning of the understanding of the laws of motion.

Another observation made by Galileo, that the time of swing of a pendulum is constant, regardless of the extent of the swing, and depends only upon the length of the pendulum itself, involved inertia and the principle that Newton embodied in his first law of motion—that a body at rest cannot get into motion of itself and that a body in motion tends to continue so with the same velocity unless it is acted upon by external forces. This law led to the idea of momentum, the product of mass and velocity. Galileo was thus able to define acceleration: "I call a motion uniformly accelerated when, starting from rest, its momentum or degree of speed increases directly as the time measured from the beginning of motion."

Newton embodied the same principle in his second law in the following words: "The time of rate of change of momentum in any direction equals the moving force impressed in that direction upon the mass particle." This second law introduces the concept of mass as opposed to weight, which was Galileo's concept. Galileo had realized, of course, that matter has weight, but he did not realize that it was desirable to have a term for the quantity of matter that a body contains apart from the acceleration to which it is exposed. The weight of a body is its mass under the acceleration of gravity. In the first paragraph of his great book on natural philosophy, however, Newton defined mass thus: "The quantity of matter is the measure of the same arising from its density and bulk conjointly. . . . It is this quantity that I mean hereafter everywhere under the name of body or mass." Thus a quantity of mass remains the same, and under acceleration by other means than gravity, the force is acting upon a given mass rather than upon a given weight since the idea of weight involves the acceleration of gravity.

To the two fundamental laws of motion, Newton added a third, which dealt with reaction and in some ways seems to be even more original than the concept of mass. Newton showed that if a given mass is attracted toward the earth with a certain force corresponding to its weight, the earth must be attracted toward the mass with the same force. When a gun is fired, for example, the shot is violently accelerated forward, but the gun is accelerated, and not too gently, backwards. Newton said: "Reaction is always equal and opposite to action; that is to say, the actions of two bodies upon each other are always equal and directly opposite." If these laws of motion had been applied only to the observation of particles upon the earth, they would have produced much less effect upon the minds of men than was actually the case. Newton applied them to the movements of the heavenly bodies and to the explanation of the laws which Kepler had deduced from those movements.

Johannes Kepler was the successor of Tycho Brahe, the great Danish astronomer. At Uranienborg in Denmark, Tycho Brahe built the first modern observatory, where by means of quadrants he observed the positions of stars and planets. It must be remembered that this was before the invention of the telescope, and these quadrants were the ancestors of the transit instruments, fixed in meridian, with which the time of passage of an object across the meridian can be observed. With these quadrants equipped with sights, Brahe made the most astonishingly accurate observations of the positions of seven hundred and seventy-seven stars.

The cosmic theory which Brahe used was a modification of Ptolemy's theory. He did not adopt the heliocentric Copernican theory because he saw that if the positions of the stars were observed six months apart, and Copernicus were right, the earth would have moved in its passage around the sun a prodigious distance in those six months and the stars should show displacement relative to each other. Brahe's observations, made with the utmost precision of which he was capable, showed no such movement; and he concluded that the earth must be at rest. This is one of the many cases to be found in the history of science where an effect which really existed was sought for but not found because the effect was too small to be detected by the method of observation used. With the development of powerful telescopes, making possible observations very much more accurate than Tycho Brahe's, the effect of the movement of the earth on its orbit can be detected in the displacement of some stars, which we now know to be the nearer ones. The effect is known as the *parallax* and is used for determining the distance of the stars. Tycho Brahe could not be expected to have realized the enormous distance of the stars in comparison even with the size of the orbit of the earth.

Kepler became Brahe's assistant and on his death succeeded to his position. Perhaps because of his poor sight, he did not continue the great campaign of observation to which Brahe had devoted his life; instead, he used Brahe's astronomical data to compute the orbits of the planets. He adopted the Copernican theory, however, which by that time had been generally accepted. According to that theory, the orbits of the planets were circles. But when Kepler studied the observations of the planet Mars, he soon realized that it did not revolve about the sun in a circle and that when it was nearest to the sun, its motion was more rapid than when it was farther away. Then he announced that the planets revolved about the sun in ellipses, with the sun at one of the foci. This was his first law. Next he showed that if a line were drawn joining a planet to the sun as the planet revolved in its orbit, the line would sweep out equal areas in equal times. Finally he gave his great third law, that the squares of the periods of revolution of the planets around the sun are proportional to the cubes of their average distances from the sun. These laws were statements of fact that Kepler derived from Brahe's observations.

When Newton took up the matter, he showed that Kepler's third law would be true provided that there were an attracting force between the sun and the planet that varied inversely as the square of the distance and that Kepler's second law could be explained by the same assumption. If the sun attracted a planet by a force varying inversely as the square of the distance, a line joining the planet to the sun would sweep out equal areas in equal times. This assumption—that there existed in the universe a force extending outward to the planets and varying inversely as the square of the distance to them—applied, of course, to all heavenly bodies; and Newton applied it to the position of the moon in its movement around the earth. He found, however, that it did not agree exactly with the observations, which involved, of course, the diameter of the earth; and for sixteen years Newton put the work aside. In 1682 it was discovered that the diameter of the earth had been measured incorrectly and was over 500 miles greater than the figure that had been adopted.* Newton immediately repeated his calculations and found that they agreed with the observed motion of the moon. He then extended the work to include the motions of the planets and their satellites, comets, and even the tides of the sea. He stated his general law of gravitation: "Every particle of matter in the universe attracts every other particle with a force that varies directly as the product of the mass and inversely as the square of the distance."

The discovery of the fundamental laws of motion was a challenge to philosophers to seek fundamental principles that would supply laws of a general nature. The mathematicians d'Alembert, Euler, Lagrange, and Laplace developed such general principles, derived from the laws of motion, which were applicable not only to material bodies but to the flow of light, heat, and electricity. On the mathematical principles that they established, the science of physics has been built. Although the physical ideas themselves have changed with the progress of experimental science, the new ideas have been expressed in terms of the same fundamental principles. In the nineteenth century, physicists thought that it might be possible to reduce all laws to the laws of mechanics.

---

* It is possible that Newton's difficulty arose instead from lack of proof that the mass of a spherical body would behave as if it were concentrated at the center.

Laplace said: "Give me the position and velocity of all the particles at a given moment and I will predict the state of the world at any future moment." The statistical theory of heat, attributed to Ludwig Boltzmann, the electromagnetic theory of light, and the "fluid" theory of electricity tended to confirm this mechanistic viewpoint.

The nature of heat attracted little attention in ancient times. Fire was one of Aristotle's four elements, and heat was considered an imponderable substance, to which Antoine Lavoisier gave the name *caloric*. That some substances should absorb heat more readily than others was ascribed to their greater power of attraction and was expressed as their having greater capacity for heat.

The first scientist to study heat systematically was Joseph Black, a chemist of Glasgow. He observed that when ice melts, it absorbs heat without undergoing any change in temperature; and Black named the heat which disappears in the process *latent heat*. Black showed that, in the melting of ice, heat was absorbed equivalent to that made available by the cooling of an equal mass of water through 140° Fahrenheit. Black also discovered that heat is used in the evaporation of water. It requires, indeed, nearly seven times as much heat to change a pound of water into steam as to melt a pound of ice.

The discovery that heat was not a substance was made by Benjamin Rumford and Humphry Davy, who showed by experiment that heat could be produced by friction. Rumford was engaged in the boring of cannon in the military workshops of Bavaria and observed the amount of heat produced by the boring tool. He arranged one experiment in which water was boiled by the heat generated in boring the metal. Davy showed that ice could be melted by friction. These experiments were made at the end of the eighteenth century. At the beginning of the nineteenth century John Dalton advanced his atomic theory (see Chapter VI, page 121), and it was realized that matter consisted of molecules and that its properties might be due to the behavior of these molecules.

Thus evolved the idea that heat is a mode of motion, the motion of the molecules; that a hot body is one in which the molecules are moving energetically; and that the latent heat of evaporation of water is the energy absorbed in giving rapid motion to the molecules leaving the liquid surface.

As a result of the work of Nicolas Carnot on the theory of the steam engine and of Julius Mayer and James Joule on the transformation of mechanical work into heat, the law of the conservation of energy was enunciated, often known as the *first law of thermodynamics:* "Energy can neither be created nor destroyed, but it may be changed from one form to another."

This principle, simple as it seems, has been one of the chief guiding principles of physics ever since it was first stated. Motion, heat, light, and electricity—all are forms of energy, and they can be transformed into each other. Indeed, the science of physics deals primarily with this transformation. With the discovery by Einstein that mass and energy also are interchangeable, that the motion of a particle involves a change in its mass—a change that becomes great only when its velocity approaches that of light—and, still more important, that the destruction of mass liberates enormous quantities of energy, the understanding of the transformations of energy became a knowledge of the physical laws of the universe. The great principle that governs transformation of energy is the *second law of thermodynamics:* In those transformations, energy loses potential. Heat, for instance, cannot of itself pass from a colder to a warmer body. Mechanical effect cannot be derived by cooling matter below the temperature of the coldest surrounding objects. The tendency of energy transformations is to diminish the difference in energy levels. The quantity of energy transferred, divided by the temperature, is called the *entropy.* And the second law of thermodynamics can be stated in the terms that the entropy of any closed system tends to increase. In mechanics and electricity the potential always decreases if no outside energy is added. A transformation in which the entropy remains constant is reversible, whereas one in which the entropy increases must be irreversible. In dealing with the transformation of energy, therefore, physicists use two variables: the energy involved and the entropy of the system. In any transformation of energy for which we wish to write the equations, the first law of thermodynamics states that the energy must remain constant after the transformation; that is, the two sides of the equation must balance. The second law of thermodynamics states that the entropy must increase in carrying out the transformation.

The attempt to reduce all laws to mechanical laws led to the statistical theory of heat, formulated by Boltzmann and very successfully applied to chemical problems by Willard Gibbs. The investigation of the states of matter (gaseous, liquid, solid) and especially of its behavior at very low temperatures (near the absolute zero) forms the basis of much research in the field of thermodynamics.

In the earliest speculations on the nature of light, Plato and Aristotle held that light is derived from the eye, and they pictured the eye as sending out something that intercepted an object and so illuminated it. This idea, however, was supplanted by the idea that the light was emitted from the object seen; and much later it was realized that light is emitted by such light sources as the sun and reflected to the eye by objects seen.

Lenses were known to the ancients. The use that was made of them is not known. Possibly the crystal lenses that have been found were considered to be merely ornamental, although the fact that they would concentrate the rays from the sun and would act as burning glasses is mentioned by Aristophanes. In medieval times lenses were certainly used as magnifying glasses to assist in reading. It is not a very long step from the use of a lens in the hand to the production of lenses in a mount that can be carried on the face and thus to the invention of spectacles; but the invention of spectacles must have been a most important step in increasing the efficiency of those suffering from the small defects of vision that are so common. Spectacles came into use in Italy about the end of the thirteenth century, and it is hard to believe that nothing else of importance was done with lenses until two were combined to form a telescope, nearly three hundred years later.

The first attempt to discuss the theory of lenses was made by Kepler, who wrote a book on the theory of the telescope. This was just after the publication of the work of Galileo and the discoveries he had made with the instrument. It is interesting that the effect of the revolutionary discovery of the telescope on Kepler was to incite him to a discussion of its theory. One can imagine how different would have been the course of events if Tycho Brahe had lived to learn of the existence of the telescope. The results of Kepler's calculations varied little from the observed facts, but he did not know the law of refraction; that is, the way in which a ray of light is deviated when it passes from air to glass. In spite of this, Kepler's work was undoubtedly very valuable in providing a basis for the design of refracting telescopes.

The correct statement of the law of refraction was given by Willebrord Snell at the University of Leyden in 1621, but his manuscript was not published at the time; and the law was embodied by Descartes, the great philosopher and mathematician, in his book on optics. Descartes, however, prefaced the statement of Snell's law with a mechanical theory of the nature of light, in which he assumed that light traveled more rapidly in denser media. Pierre de Fermat, the French mathematician who formulated the theory of numbers, deduced the law of refraction from exactly the opposite assumption, namely, that light travels more slowly in denser media, and announced the great principle known ever since by his name—that a ray of light originating at a point in one medium will travel to a point in another medium by the path which requires the minimum of time. Of all principles in optics, this has been perhaps the most fruitful.

As in mechanics, the great scientist who advanced the whole theory of optics was Isaac Newton. Newton showed experimentally that a prism splits a ray of light refracted through it into a band of colors. White light could therefore be considered to contain rays of various degrees of refrangibility, the least refrangible rays being red and the most refrangible, violet. Thus Newton discovered the spectrum and with it much relating to the nature of color. Newton made another observation which later became of the utmost importance, namely, that when a thin film of air occurs between two plates of glass, the film shows colors, and these colors depend upon the thickness of the film.

The distinction between the physical and the psychological properties of color was first made clear at the beginning of the nineteenth century by Thomas Young, who advanced a theory of color vision according to which the eye perceives three fundamental sensations—red, green, and violet—and all other color sensations arise from combinations of these three. Yellow, for instance, arises from simultaneous sensations of red and green. The distinction between the psychological basis of color and its physical basis in the differing refrangibility of the rays of light has been a difficulty for scientific workers and artists ever since the days of Newton. The pigments of the artists have as their fundamental colors the complementaries to Young's sensation primaries, and only with the advance of color photography in recent years have the relations between the sensation primaries and the pigment colors become familiar to the general public.

As a result of his work on the refraction of light through prisms, Newton inferred that the dispersion of a prism is always proportional to the deviation it produces; that is, he didn't realize that by the use of glass of different kinds prisms could be made that for a given refraction would give different deviations between the rays of varying colors. Newton concluded that it was not possible to correct the variation in the focal length of a lens for different colors, an effect which is generally known as the *chromatic aberration* of the lens. He abandoned the idea of making telescopes of great power by means of lenses and invented reflecting telescopes, using mirrors to avoid the difficulty with chromatic aberration.

It was shown experimentally about the middle of the eighteenth century that Newton had been wrong and that achromatic lenses could be made. The whole subject was put on a solid foundation by Fraunhofer, who in 1817 discovered that in the solar spectrum there were certain dark lines that enabled him to identify the positions of the colors of the spectrum with accuracy and to measure with precision the refractive indices of glass for light of different colors.

Joseph von Fraunhofer was able to calculate the principles required for the achromatism of the telescope and made an excellent refractor of 9½-inch aperture to be used by the astronomers of Dorpat Observatory. Fraunhofer also made optical glass and was really the first working optical instrument maker of the modern school.

While the use of light in optical instruments was advancing, the nature of light continued to engage the minds of men. Newton had devoted much thought to the dynamics of particles, and it is not surprising that he considered light to consist of material particles emitted from heated bodies and producing a mechanical effect by their action on the eye. A phenomenon observed by Francesco Grimaldi, however, was difficult to reconcile with any theory that considered light to consist of particles, that is, that if a point source of light illuminates a sharp straight edge, such as a knife blade, the shadow will be bounded by a series of light and dark bands. To this phenomenon Grimaldi gave the very appropriate name of *diffraction,* by which it is still known. Diffraction had also been observed by Robert Hooke, the energetic and versatile secretary of the Royal Society, who concluded that there was some kind of vibrating motion in light. Thus Newton was induced to suggest that the corpuscles of light embodied a vibratory element. The rays of light, for instance, in passing by the edges of bodies might be bent backwards and forwards several times "with a motion like that of an eel."

Another observation of the greatest importance in understanding the nature of light was the discovery, as a result of observations of the eclipses of the satellites of Jupiter by the body of the planet, that light did not travel with infinite speed. Indeed, in 1676 Olaus Römer calculated from these observations that the velocity of light was about one hundred and ninety thousand miles a second, a value little different from the value used today.

The great opponent of Newton's theory of the emission of light as particles was Christiaan Huygens, the Dutch astronomer who first made accurate clocks by the use of the pendulum and discovered the double refraction of Iceland spar and the refraction of the light of the stars by the atmosphere. Huygens regarded light as being non-material because of its great velocity of propagation and because two rays traversing the same path in contrary directions do not hinder each other. He therefore adopted the theory that light consists of wave motions in a hypothetical medium that is called the *ether*. The properties of the ether are deduced from the properties of light. Huygens considered each point of a luminous body to be the origin of elementary spherical waves, of which the envelope corresponds at any instant to the position of the wave front. Thus, as the wave front travels forward with the velocity of light, it could always be considered as the envelope of an infinite number of elementary waves. The perpendicular to the wave front corresponds to what is termed a *ray*.

Newton's corpuscular theory and Huygens' wave theory are equally adapted to describe the phenomena of reflection and refraction. The literature of the eighteenth century is full of discussion of the two theories, but in 1827 W. B. Hamilton proved that they are only different aspects of the same mathematical laws which can be derived from de Fermat's principle. The wave surfaces can be considered as the potential surfaces of the light rays, and the light rays as the normals of the wave surfaces. None of these theories alone, however, can explain the phenomena of diffraction and interference.

They involve a periodic disturbance moving along the rays from wave surface to wave surface. Two rays or two waves coming from the same point source can be united in a point in such a way that the maximum of one wave will coincide with the minimum of the other and so neutralize it. Thus two waves of light can, under certain circumstances, produce darkness. This idea was given definite form in 1801 by Thomas Young. Before this, the corpuscular theory of light had been generally accepted for almost a century, largely because it had been sponsored by Isaac Newton. Young founded his views on the nature of light on the following hypotheses:

A luminous body produces waves in a medium, the ether, which pervades the entire universe. Different colors of light owe their differences to the frequency of their vibrations, which produce different sensations in the retina. The production of darkness by the mutual action of two waves of light Young described as *interference;* and he was able to measure and explain by the wave theory both the diffraction fringes discovered by Grimaldi and the colors of thin films discovered by Newton. Young measured the length of the waves of light, finding that the limit of the spectrum in the red corresponded to waves about 0.0007 millimeter long, while the violet rays at the other end of the spectrum had a length of 0.0004 millimeter.

Young's theory was improved by Augustin Fresnel, who considered that the waves moving along the rays were transverse waves, vibrations in the plane perpendicular to the path of the light. This made it possible to explain not only diffraction and interference but also the phenomenon of polarization, which had been discovered in 1809 by E. L. Malus, a French physicist, who had observed that light reflected by a mirror at an incidence angle of about 57° is totally polarized, that is, it has vibrations only in the direction normal to the ray in the plane of reflection. A second reflection from a plane at right angles to the first will extinguish the light. Malus had then directed his attention to the double refraction of Iceland spar and had found that both rays are polarized, the planes of polarization being at right angles to each other. Fresnel's theory explained both interference and polarization and gave the mathematical relations for all these phenomena. Fresnel thought of the vibrations of light as vibrations of the ether, which now assumed contradictory qualities because the great velocity of light made necessary the idea that the ether was a solid of enormous rigidity, while at the same time it imposed no resistance to the passage of matter such as the planets.

Much of the theoretical work of the nineteenth century was concerned with the discussion of the properties of the ether and its relation to matter, but the greatest advance in the whole theory of radiation came with the suggestion in 1864 by J. Clark Maxwell that light was an electromagnetic phenomenon. Maxwell investigated mathematically the propagation of electric and magnetic forces in space and found the velocity of propagation to be identical with the known velocity of light and the calculated properties—those actually exhibited by light. He showed that in electromagnetic waves the electric and magnetic vibrations occur at right angles to each other and to the direction of the ray, which is, of course, normal to the waves of light, and that electromagnetic waves would be capable of being polarized and would show the phenomena of refraction, reflection, and interference. Thus he considered light an electromagnetic phenomenon corresponding to a restricted range of wave lengths; and he concluded that longer waves might exist which were far too long to be seen by the eye but could conceivably be detected by other means.

This theory was confirmed experimentally by Heinrich Hertz in 1887, and the electric waves discovered by him are those now used in radio communication. The whole range of electromagnetic radiation between the radio waves, many meters long, and the waves of light has been generated and observed. Moreover, the discovery of waves shorter than those of visible light, known as *ultraviolet waves,* was followed by the detection of waves too short to pass through the air and then by the proof that the x-rays (page 106) are very short electromagnetic waves of the same nature as light waves. As we shall see later, the most recent work on the nature of electromagnetic waves has brought us back to the conception that all waves are associated with particles and that the long controversy between the wave theory and the corpuscular theory can be resolved to some extent in a compromise.

Only two manifestations of the properties of electricity were known to the ancients. They knew that magnetite ore would attract and be attracted by iron and that amber when rubbed would attract light particles, straw, paper, etc. In the Middle Ages it was found that a suspended piece of magnetite would point north and south, and the mariner's compass was invented. At the time when Galileo was working in Florence, an English physician, William Gilbert, was carrying out experiments on the magnet and the attracting properties of substances which had been rubbed, and he showed that the behavior of the compass was due to the fact that the earth itself was a great magnet. Gilbert also found that other substances than amber—glass, sulfur, and resin—would attract light particles after they had been rubbed. He wrote the first textbook on electrical science, in which he discussed his experiments.

At the beginning of the eighteenth century, Stephen Gray found that an electric charge, the existence of which was known by its capacity for attracting particles, could move along a thread, and he even transferred such a charge along a hemp thread a thousand feet long suspended by threads of silk placed at intervals. Then, when the thread was suspended by metal wires, the charge vanished, being conducted away by the wires. In 1729 Gray discovered that an electrified glass tube would induce a charge in another tube close by but not touching it, and a number of experimenters continued to study the nature of isolated electric charges and the properties of static electricity. Electric machines for producing powerful charges by means of induction were designed, and the Leyden jar was invented, in which two conducting layers were separated by the glass of the jar, so that opposite charges could be stored on the two faces of the glass. Interest in static electricity was greatly stimulated by the spectacular results obtained. Benjamin Franklin discovered that the charges in the jar reside on the glass walls, and he built a condenser using a series of glass plates separated by sheets of tin foil, thus obtaining the condenser which we use today.

All this work dealt with static electricity, and it was not until the close of the eighteenth century that electricity in motion was investigated. Luigi Galvani, an Italian anatomist, observed that under the stimulation of an electric charge a frog's legs isolated from the body would show contraction and that it could be produced by the simple contact of two different metals moistened by the salty juices of a frog's body. Galvani, in fact, discovered the possibility of producing an electric current, for which the frog's leg was the detector. This discovery was followed up by Alessandro Volta, who in 1800 announced his voltaic pile, which consisted of a series of alternate copper and zinc plates separated by pieces of paper or flannel moistened with brine. This was the first battery, and experimenters soon designed improved batteries and were able to get electric currents with which chemical effects could be produced. Water was decomposed into hydrogen and oxygen, and Davy, experimenting at the Royal Institution, decomposed potash with a battery of two hundred and fifty cells and obtained the metal potassium. Later he prepared sodium, calcium, barium, strontium, and magnesium. With two thousand cells, he produced the first arc lamp and in the arc melted refractory substances such as platinum and quartz.

In 1819, Hans Oersted of the University of Copenhagen made a discovery which is the foundation of the science of electromagnetism. He found that a wire carrying a current would displace a compass needle when it was parallel to it and thus demonstrated that a conductor bearing an electric current produces a magnetic field. Oersted's experiments were immediately followed by those of a great Frenchman, André Ampère, who within a few months of Oersted's announcement found that two parallel electric currents would behave like magnets, attracting and repelling each other, according to the direction in which they flowed. In 1823 Ampère published a paper setting forth the mathematical theory of the effects of electromagnetism.

The inverse effect to Oersted's was not discovered for some years. It was in 1831 that Michael Faraday found that the movement of an electric circuit in a magnetic field caused a current to start in the circuit, so that just as Oersted had shown that a current produced a magnetic field, Faraday showed that a magnetic field would produce a current. As a result of this discovery, it became possible to generate electricity mechanically by the rotation of coils of wire in the field of a magnet. This is the arrangement known as the *dynamo;* and the inverse arrangement, in which the passage of electricity through a coil in a magnetic field causes it to rotate, is the *electric motor.* Thus, by the middle of the nineteenth century, from the work of Ampère, Michael Faraday, and Joseph Henry in the United States, the general nature of current electricity and especially the properties of circuits carrying direct current were completely unraveled. The development of alternating-current electricity belongs to the field of engineering rather than of physics. It is the work of the electrical engineers in the second half of the nineteenth century that made possible the great use of electricity in practical applications. Electric light, the telegraph, the telephone, and so forth represent applications of early discoveries relating to electric currents by a large group of scientists and an even greater group of engineers.

The nature of electricity itself long remained completely hidden. Its elucidation came not from further work in relation to electricity itself, but from the study of the conduction of electricity through gases. As early as 1785, William Morgan in a paper before the Royal Society referred to the glow that could be obtained when electricity was passed through an evacuated glass vessel. But the earliest systematic research on the subject was that of Faraday, who in 1836 began to study the passage of electricity through gases. He observed that if two electrodes were sealed into a bulb that was then evacuated, and electricity was passed through it from a frictional electricity machine, there appeared what he described as a "light" proceeding from the negative electrode. Faraday was limited both in the supply of electricity from his frictional machine and in the vacuum that he could obtain by the use of a piston pump.

Improved methods of obtaining high vacuum by filling the bulbs with carbon dioxide and then absorbing it with caustic potash made possible greater experimental progress. J. Gassiot in 1859 described experiments in which he undoubtedly obtained the beam that became known as a *cathode ray*. The passage of electricity through exhausted tubes containing a small amount of gas became very popular as a demonstration, and Heinrich Geissler, a German glass blower, became so skillful in the preparation of the tubes that they are known as *Geissler tubes*.

Another technical development was the introduction by Ruhmkorff in Paris of the induction coil, which facilitated the production of high electrical voltages. In 1869 J. W. Hittorf published a first communication on electrical conductivity in gases. This work was concerned with what he calls the *negative discharge,* now called the *cathode rays*. He pictured it as thin, flexible filaments, carrying currents, that could be deviated by a magnetic field and that, by a suitable arrangement of the field, could be focused, and he observed an intense heating at the focus. Hittorf also discovered the use of the incandescent cathode, with which a current could be maintained through the tube with a very small voltage.

Hittorf's experiments were repeated by William Crookes, who carried out a very large number of observations on electrical charges and exhausted tubes. Crookes showed that the cathode rays had sufficient momentum to drive a small paddle wheel of light metal built inside the tube, which led to his conclusion that the cathode rays consisted of small particles. Like Hittorf, he found that the rays could be deviated by a magnet, and as a consequence they must consist of charged particles. When they fell on an extra electrode inserted in the tube, they charged it negatively. Moreover, their velocity could be determined and was found to be very high, in some cases approaching the velocity of light. Crookes suggested that the cathode rays consisted of a new form of matter.

In 1892 H. Hertz, who had discovered the long wave electromagnetic waves, which are used in radio work, published a paper in which he showed that cathode rays can pass through thin metal foils. Two years later, P. Lenard made a tube containing a thin aluminum window, through which the cathode rays could escape into the air. At that time Wilhelm Roentgen was professor of physics at the University of Wurzburg. He covered an ordinary Hittorf vacuum tube with black paper, probably to see whether Lenard's rays could escape into the open from an ordinary glass tube. He noticed that barium platinocyanide crystals glowed by fluorescence in the dark room, although there was black paper between the tube and the crystals, and realized that some rays from the tube must penetrate the black paper. Then he found that these rays would affect a photographic plate, would pass through matter generally, and so enable the structure of things to be photographed as shadows. This work was the very important discovery of the x-rays. It had been missed by many earlier experimenters. Perhaps Morgan had actually produced x-rays in his experiments a hundred years before Roentgen recognized them. Hittorf and Crookes certainly must have produced x-rays hundreds of times, and Crookes actually fogged a box of photographic plates in his laboratory. It was only when he heard of Roentgen's discovery many years later that he understood that his plates had been fogged by the x-rays produced from his own vacuum tubes.

When Thomson showed later that the cathode stream in an exhausted tube is a stream of electrons, it was realized that electrons falling on a target, such as the end of the tube, cause x-rays to be emitted, and targets were then placed in the tubes so that the cathode stream was focused on them. The early x-ray tubes had a hemispherical cathode and a target or *anticathode,* as it was called, made of platinum. These tubes were exhausted to a high vacuum, but not too high, as otherwise the current would not pass.

In 1884 J. J. Thomson became the Cavendish professor of physics at the University of Cambridge, and as his first major piece of work he started to study the cathode rays to determine whether they were of a wave nature, similar to light, or whether, as Crookes believed, they consisted of particles carrying a charge of electricity. Thomson wrote many years afterward: *

> I had for a long time been convinced that these rays were charged particles, but it was some time before I had any suspicion that they were anything but charged atoms. My first doubts as to this being the case arose when I measured the deflection of the rays by a magnet, for this was far greater than I could account for by any hypothesis which seemed at all reasonable if the particles had a mass at all approaching that of the hydrogen atom, the smallest then known.

By measuring both the magnetic deviation and the total energy of the rays, using a thermocouple to find their heating effect, Thomson was able to calculate the velocity of the rays and the ratio of the mass of the particles to the electric charge. The conclusion showed that the velocity was enormously high—5 per cent of the velocity of light, much higher than could be expected for any molecule or atom—and that the ratio of the mass to the charge was much less than would be possible for hydrogen atoms. If the rays consisted of electrified particles, the particles were something quite new to

* Lord Rayleigh, *Sir J. J. Thomson,* p. 80, Cambridge University Press, 1942.

science. That they were due to particles was shown by the
fact that they could be deviated by a transverse electrostatic
field. Tests on this subject had failed previously because the
gas pressure in the tube was too high. In 1897, then, Thomson finally showed that the cathode rays consist of charged
particles and that these particles are very small—about one
two-thousandth of the mass of the hydrogen atom. The name
electron had already been given to the atom of negative electricity by Johnstone Stoney in 1874, at the time that he put
forward his idea of atomistic electricity. It was now realized
that the particles of the cathode rays are electrons.

Another application of this method of using electro-mag-
netic and electrostatic fields to control a stream of electricity in a vacuum was applied to the positively charged
streams that come from the anode. These positive rays can
be deviated by a magnetic field and also by an electrical field,
but the amount of the deviation is much less than that of the
cathode rays because the particles from the anode are much
heavier than those from the cathode. They can be shown to
consist of streams of atoms or molecules. Moreover, such a
stream contains a number of different atoms, and since these
are of different mass, they will be separated by the magnetic
field. This work was done by Thomson and his student
F. W. Aston. Later, Aston designed an instrument which
he called the *mass spectrograph,* in which the positive ray
passed through a magnetic field so that the atoms of different mass were separated, the streams of different atoms being
detected either by their record on a photographic film or by
the measurement of the ionizing power of the stream when
allowed to run into a chamber containing gas of which the
conductivity could be measured. A very important result of
Aston's work was the discovery that frequently several atoms
of the same element exist having different masses. Thus, in
the case of neon, one of the first elements to be investigated,
about 90 per cent of the gas consists of atoms having a mass
of 20, whereas 10 per cent consists of atoms having a mass
of 22 units. Atoms having the same chemical properties but

different masses are known as *isotopic* elements. As a result of Thomson's work, the general nature of electricity became clear, and it was realized that a current of electricity was a current of electrons, which are the atoms of electricity in the sense that they are the smallest unit of electricity known. Each electron carries its unit charge, while its mass is approximately one two-thousandth of that of the atom of hydrogen.

The elucidation of the nature of electricity had two results of the utmost importance. It made possible a new field of electrical engineering, which has become generally known as *electronics*. It also made possible the understanding of the structure of the chemical atoms and of the nature of radio-activity, and this we shall deal with later.

The engineering applications of electronics depend upon the use of streams of electrons to control electric circuits. The first observation which led to this was made by Edison, who observed that when he sealed two elements into a lamp and heated one of them by a current, the second filament in the vacuum received electricity across the space from the heated filament. This was before the work of Thomson, but we now see that what Edison observed was the passage of electrons across the vacuum from the heated filament to the cold one. Edison did not follow up the observation, but it was studied by others, notably by J. A. Fleming and by Lee de Forest, who had the idea of introducing into the space between the two filaments a grid of wires, by charging which he could control the flow of electrons across the space.

The electronic tubes, now so widely used, are essentially valves which control the flow of electric current through a circuit as a valve controls the flow of water through a pipe. When a valve tube is put into an electric circuit, the circuit is broken because, in the tube, there is an open space across which the electrons must pass in order to maintain the flow of current through the circuit. At this point the current can be controlled. For example, if an alternating current is applied to the tube, the anode at which the electrons are received becomes alternately positively and negatively charged.

When it is positively charged, the anode will attract the electrons, and the current will flow. When it is negatively charged, it will repel the electrons and no current will flow, so that an alternating current applied to a valve tube will be transformed into a pulsating current in one direction, the pulsations in the opposite direction being suppressed by the tube. Then if a grid is inserted in the tube, the flow of the electrons can be controlled by the charge on the grid. If a signal current is applied to the grid, the flow of electrons through the tube will follow the signal current, and in this way a small signal current can be enormously amplified by means of a tube.

In the so-called *photo tubes,* electrons are emitted when light falls on the cathode, and thus a beam of light can control an electric current which will follow the variations in the light. By means of a photo tube, we can transform light signals into electric signals and then by means of amplifying tubes increase the electric currents so that they can perform all sorts of operations. In this way, the reproduction of sound can be accomplished. The sound waves can be used in a microphone to control an electric current that can make a lamp glow, and the variation of the intensity of the light will therefore correspond to the sound. This variation can be recorded photographically on a film. Light passing through the record can be used to produce a current in a photo tube, and this current can be amplified to operate a loud speaker, by which the sound can be reproduced.

W. D. Coolidge, working in the research laboratory of the General Electric Company, improved the x-ray tube very much by using a hot cathode, from which electrons were emitted even in a vacuum too high for the passage of electricity from a cold cathode, and by using a heavy tungsten target that could withstand the powerful beam instead of the thin platinum target used previously. At the same time, the machines used to generate the electricity were greatly improved, and in this way x-ray sources of great intensity were made available.

The nature of the x-rays was a subject of discussion for many years after their discovery. It seemed equally probable that the x-rays consisted of streams of particles having some analogy to the cathode rays and that they might be waves similar to light waves. The x-rays could not be refracted, as light is, by dense media, and for a time all attempts to diffract them failed. Finally, Max von Laue, the director of the Institute of Theoretical Physics in Berlin, showed that a diffraction pattern could be produced from a beam of x-rays by the use of a natural crystal. It was generally agreed that x-rays represented an electromagnetic radiation similar to that of light but of much shorter wave length, the x-rays from a tungsten target having a wave length about one five-thousandth that of visible light.

The discovery of the x-rays was followed by the discovery of radioactivity and the identification of the alpha particles emitted by radium with doubly charged helium atoms by Sir Ernest Rutherford.* This work on radioactivity focused Rutherford's attention on the structure of the atom, and in 1913 he suggested that atoms were made up of a nucleus containing practically the whole of the mass of the atom and a number of electrons rotating in orbits around the central nucleus which were sufficient to neutralize the charge on the nucleus and thus insure an electrically neutral atom. Rutherford was led to this view of the structure of the atom by experiments on the deviation of rays, particularly the alpha rays, when they collided with atoms, just as something could be learned about the shape of a building by the way in which balls thrown at it bounced.

At the same time, Niels Bohr was studying another property of atoms, the spectra which they emit when they are excited by the passage of electricity. When atoms are excited electrically, as gases in a vacuum tube or an electric arc for instance, they emit spectra which are not continuous, like those of hot bodies, but consist of isolated lines. Some of

* Chapter VI, p. 136.

these spectra are very complex. The wave length of the lines emitted can be measured, and certain numerical relationships between them had been deduced as the result of a long study of the problem by many workers. A mechanism for the emission of a spectrum by a given element was still lacking when Bohr took up the problem. In 1913 he suggested that the action in the atom that resulted in the emission of a spectral line was the movement of one of the rotating electrons from one orbit to another. Taking Rutherford's picture of the atom, in which the electrons rotate around a nucleus, Bohr assumed that as long as the electron rotated in a given orbit, it would not radiate any energy; but that if it changed its orbit and shifted to a smaller one, energy would be set free and would be emitted as a spectral line. Moreover, the orbits of the electrons would be at discrete definite distances from the nucleus. The radii of these orbits would, in fact, be proportional to the squares of successive whole numbers—1, 4, 9, 16, etc. Consequently, whenever an electron shifts from one orbit to another, it emits energy of a definite amount, which corresponds, of course, to a definite wave length in the light emitted.

The idea that energy was emitted by atoms in definitely fixed amounts, corresponding to the change in diameter of the electron orbits, supplied a mechanism for a general law of radiation that had been announced by Max Planck about ten years before—that radiation is emitted in definite units, so to speak, atoms of energy, which Planck named *quanta*. Bohr, using Rutherford's idea of the atom, supplied a mechanism for Planck's quantum theory of radiation. The structure of the Bohr-Rutherford atom has undergone some modification since it was originally suggested. It has become established, however, as a basic principle and has been able to explain a great many different phenomena, such as the radiation of hot bodies, the emission of spectra, the absorption spectra of molecules, the chemical structure of compounds, the effect upon atoms of radiation, and the radioactive elements and their behavior.

Planck's atomic theory of the structure of energy led to a revival of the old argument as to whether radiation was in the form of waves or of streams of particles. According to Planck, radiation was in quanta, each of which had an energy content of hv, where h is a universal constant and v is the frequency, that is, the inverse of the wave length, of the radiation. This involved a discussion of the physical structure of these quanta—whether they consisted, for instance, of short trains of waves, since the wave structure was implicit in the definition of frequency. Another form of radiation is that of the cathode ray; it is known to consist of streams of electrons.

Louis V. de Broglie, a gifted French amateur who has devoted his life to research in physics, suggested that if the structure of radiant energy, which is associated with wave length, had an atomic and discontinuous nature, then matter, which obviously is atomic and discontinuous, might also have properties associated with waves. This was confirmed by the experiments of C. J. Davisson and L. H. Germer in the Bell Telephone Research Laboratory. They succeeded in diffracting electron beams, work which has been followed by the development of the electron microscope, in which a beam of electrons forms images parallel to those formed by light in a microscope. The two aspects of radiation were finally reconciled by the work of W. Heisenberg and of Erwin Schroedinger, who took up the old ideas of Hamilton with regard to the dualistic aspect of rays and waves and initiated the physical theories classed as *quantum mechanics,* into which they introduced the theory of probability.

The theory of radiation and of the structure of matter has been greatly affected by the development of the relativity theory of Einstein. The adoption of the ether by Augustin Fresnel and Clark Maxwell as the medium in which radiation is transmitted led to the suggestion that, since the earth was moving through the ether, the velocity of light as measured by an observer on the earth should be different if it were measured in the direction of the earth's travel or across that direction. This was tested by Albert Michelson in a series of very careful investigations and no difference was found. Repetitions of the experiment with Edward Morley, from which it is generally known as the Michelson-Morley experiment, gave essentially the same result. The ether is stationary with regard to the earth, and, at the same time, no evidence can be found that it is dragged with the planets. The first solution of this paradox was given by Einstein in his special relativity theory, in which he re-examined the foundations of Newtonian mechanics.

The conception of space and time as independent frameworks presupposes that we can compare time in different points of space, and that the meaning of simultaneity at points separated in space can be clearly defined. If we had instantaneous signals, this would be self-evident; but even light needs time to travel from one point to another. Einstein took the fundamental result of the Michelson-Morley experiment, that light has a velocity independent of the motion of the observer, as the basis of his new theory. With the help of this definition, we can define the simultaneity of two events for a given observer. The laws of physics become laws in space-time. The difference from classical physics is given by a correction factor $\sqrt{1 - \dfrac{v^2}{c^2}}$ wherein c is the velocity of light and v the relative velocity of the object with respect to the observer. Since the velocities of matter are mostly very small compared to the velocity of light, the correction factor can be neglected in most practical cases, thus leaving the bulk of physical experience uncorrected. However, it has served to explain some phenomena, such as the motion of the perihelion of Mercury, and is of importance in connection with the structure of spectral lines that arise from the motion of electrons.

The classical laws of motion teach that no physical experiment can distinguish a state of uniform velocity from a state of rest. The rapid and complicated movement of a point on the earth, for instance, is not felt as movement by the inhabitants of the earth in spite of the fact that the point is rotating around the center of the earth with a velocity at the equator of over a thousand miles an hour. It is also moving around the sun with a velocity of about eighteen miles a second, and the whole solar system is moving among the stars with even higher velocity, the rotation of the galaxy corresponding to a velocity for the solar system of over one hundred miles a second. To the occupant of a point on the earth, all these motions are unperceived as motion. Einstein expanded his special theory and stated in his general theory of relativity that even accelerated motion cannot be ascertained by physical experiment. Sitting in an elevator that is completely sealed, an observer cannot distinguish whether the elevator is moving with accelerated velocity or whether it is resting in a gravitational field. Einstein's general relativity theory uses this idea to reduce all physical laws to one, namely, de Fermat's law that the path between two events separating two points in space-time has stationary value compared with other paths possible in the gravitational fields given by all the effective forces. This theory allows the laws of classical physics to be expressed in a very simple form; moreover, it makes it possible to relate mass to energy. For the transformation of mass into energy, Einstein deduced the relation $E = \Delta mc^2$, where Δm is the change in the mass in grams, E the energy produced in ergs, and c is the velocity of light. Since the velocity of light is 3×10^{10} centimeters per second, $c^2 = 9 \times 10^{20}$.

Attempts to introduce the atomic structure of matter and energy into a general field theory have not yet been successful. At the present time we have dual theories in all fields of physics—a relativistic continuous field theory, which uses disturbances (waves) periodic in time and space and explains the phenomena of interference, polarization, and diffraction, common to all matter and all forms of energy; and an atomic theory of matter and energy, which is basically discontinuous and the laws of which are statistical in nature.

From the time of Newton to the beginning of the twentieth century, astronomy was the science of position. It dealt with the positions of the stars and with the movement of the planets in the solar system. Astronomers spent the greater part of their time in the computation of positions and in the verification of their results. The greatest triumph of that period was the calculation of the existence and orbit of a planet beyond Uranus, a result obtained from slight deviations between the observed position of Uranus and that which was calculated from the influence of the other planets, and the verification of this discovery by the observation of Neptune when the telescope was directed to the calculated position.

On the nature of the stars and the constitution of the stellar universe, there was much speculation, but few facts seemed to be obtainable. As an example of a thing that must forever remain unknown, August Comte quoted the chemical composition of the heavenly bodies. All this was changed by the application of the spectroscope to astronomy. Von Fraunhofer had observed that in the spectrum of the sun there were black lines, and Robert Bunsen and Gustav Kirchhoff showed that these corresponded in position to the bright lines in the emission spectra of some of the elements. One of these was so unmistakable that its identification was certain—the double line in the yellow, to which was assigned the letter D by von Fraunhofer, corresponding exactly to the double emission line of sodium in the yellow. Jules Janssen and Norman Lockyer, pioneers in astronomical spectroscopy, observed in the spectrum of the chromosphere a bright yellow line slightly on the green side of the D line, which they ascribed to an unknown element; and Lockyer, greatly daring, named this element from the sun, *helium*. In 1896 William Ramsay, who had identified argon in the earth's atmosphere,* was looking for argon in the gas occluded in certain minerals when the spectroscope showed him that the long-sought-for helium had been found.

* Chapter VI, p. 134.

With the application of the spectroscope to the study of the stars, the science of astrophysics was born. The chemical composition of the atmospheres of the stars could be analyzed, and in the case of the sun the most detailed investigations were possible since the solar spectrum can be examined with a dispersion and on a scale possible for no other source of energy. With the increasing power of the great reflecting telescopes and of the spectroscopes attached to them, it was possible to learn much more about the structure of the stellar universe.

Scattered through the sky and appearing on photographic plates among the stars are patches of radiant material to which has been given the name *nebulae.* The spectroscope shows that some of these nebulae are glowing masses of gas because their spectra are quite different from those of the stars. They show the bright emission lines corresponding to those emitted by a gas through which electricity is passing in a vacuum tube. But by far the greater number of the nebulae have spectra that correspond to what might be termed an average stellar spectrum, especially those nebulae that have a definite shape, often a spiral. In the greatest of all these nebulae, that in the constellation Andromeda, the 100-inch telescope at Mount Wilson has shown the existence of stars. It was possible from the nature of the stars observed to calculate the distance of the Andromeda nebula, and it proved to be nearly a million light-years away.

Man has traveled far from Tycho Brahe's picture of the universe. First the earth lost its place at the center of the solar system. Then it was realized that the sun was but one star in the Milky Way, although, indeed, for a time it had been believed that the sun and, therefore, the earth were near the middle of the Milky Way. Now, with the Andromeda nebula before our eyes, it is clear that the whole Milky Way system is a great spiral nebula and that it is not alone in the universe. There are other spiral nebulae composed of multitudes of stars like those of the Milky Way. The Andromeda nebula itself may be as great in its extension as our galaxy.

More and more, as these galaxies are being observed, it becomes clear that there are enormous numbers of galaxies and that we have to think of the universe not as composed of millions of stars but as composed of millions of galaxies, each composed of hundreds of millions of stars.

When a star is observed with a spectroscope, the absorption lines corresponding to certain elements are not found at exactly the same wave length as those lines show in the laboratory. The explanation of this was given as long ago as 1842 by Christian Doppler, who showed that if a luminous body is moving in the line of sight, the frequency of the light emitted will be changed by its velocity. If a star is coming toward us, we shall receive more light waves of a given ray in a given time than if the star were standing still. The frequency, therefore, of the light will be increased, and a spectral line will be moved toward the blue. If the star is moving away from us, the spectral line will move toward the red. When the light of the most distant nebulae was observed, it was found that the lines were strongly displaced toward the red and that this displacement increased in proportion to the faintness of the nebula and therefore presumably in proportion to its distance. The effect is so great that the picture obtained is that of an exploding universe, one in which the outer nebulae are retreating in all directions as if the whole universe were expanding. The mathematical astronomers have analyzed the suggestion that the universe may be considered to be expanding, using as their basis Einstein's general theory of relativity, in which the four-dimensional universe involving the three dimensions of space and time may be considered a closed system and the expansion of this closed system can be reconciled with the principles of the general field theory.

Chapter VI

THE GROWTH OF CHEMICAL IDEAS

The fundamental principles of chemistry date not from the seventeenth but from the end of the eighteenth and the beginning of the nineteenth centuries. The delay in the development of chemistry may be ascribed to two different causes. The minor one is that experimental chemistry demands access to equipment and materials to a much greater extent than experimental physics. Galileo and Newton were able to conduct experiments with very little apparatus in ordinary buildings, and even in the nineteenth century Lord Rayleigh was famous for the skill with which he made observations of the greatest precision with apparatus which he had constructed from pieces of wire, wood, and sealing wax. But chemistry is the study of reactions, and it is necessary to have materials which react and then to place them in suitable environments, as, for instance, by heating them. Today we take for granted a supply of pure chemical reagents, and we can use very convenient methods of applying heat by gas burners or electric furnaces. In the days when there were no electricity and no gas, heat could be obtained only by burning wood or coal, and no supply of suitable heatproof glassware was available. It was necessary for the chemist in most cases to prepare his own materials, and these were usually very impure. Within our own lifetime, indeed, work in organic chemistry has been delayed by the inaccessibility of starting materials and has only recently been facilitated by their supply. A second and more important cause of the delay in the advance of experimental chemistry was that it got off to a wrong start twice. The earliest chemists were alchemists, who were attempting to find the philosophers' stone or to transmute metals. They were, in fact, anxious to work on applied chemistry, and their efforts to apply chemistry instead of observing and studying the facts delayed the discovery of the nature of the reactions that constitute the science of chemistry. Then when experimental chemistry got under way, in the seventeenth century, its progress was greatly delayed by an entirely incorrect hypothesis that was adopted.

George Ernst Stahl, physician to the King of Prussia, studied the phenomena of combustion and accepted the idea suggested by J. J. Becker, one of the last alchemists, that they were due to the loss by the burning substance of the principle of combustibility, to which he gave the name *phlogiston*. When flame is observed escaping from a piece of burning wood, what is more reasonable than to assume that the principle that renders the material combustible is escaping in the flame? And this was the more reasonable because the alchemists had laid great stress on the existence of various principles in all things, the principle of combustibility being generally termed *sulfur* by the alchemists. We now know, of course, that combustion is the combination of the burning substance with the oxygen of the air, but this idea was completely reversed by the followers of the phlogiston theory, even though measurements of the change of weight during combustion showed that the burning substance increased in weight. This was explained by the *ad hoc* assumption that phlogiston had a negative weight. Even Joseph Priestley, the English nonconformist minister who discovered oxygen gas in 1774 simultaneously with Karl Scheele, insisted on calling it *dephlogisticated air,* his idea being that this was the component of the atmosphere with which the phlogiston united when it escaped from a burning substance.

The true nature of combustion was demonstrated by Lavoisier in 1772 as a result of quantitative measurements, in which he found that the burning of sulfur and phosphorus and the oxidation of metals resulted in an increase of weight. He then repeated Joseph Priestley's experiments on the heating of mercuric oxide to obtain oxygen and showed that combustion was due to a combination of the material with oxygen. In 1789, the year of the French revolution, Lavoisier published the work on which all chemistry is founded today and freed the chemical world from its obsession with the phlogiston theory, which had delayed its progress for so long.

All the early work in chemistry had been concerned with the nature of reaction, and after the experiments of Lavoisier, which elucidated the properties of oxygen and its reaction with hydrogen, carbon, and other elements, rapid progress was made toward understanding not merely the nature of reactions but the quantitative laws which govern them, so that the principles of quantitative analysis could be laid down. As a result of this, J. L. Proust, a French chemist who was director of the Royal Laboratory in Madrid, was able to show that a definite chemical compound always contains the same elements combined in the same proportions by weight. This *law of definite proportions* was the basis on which Dalton founded his atomic theory.

John Dalton was a teacher of mathematics, physics, and chemistry, chiefly in Manchester, but, as he says in his brief biography, "occasionally by invitation in other places; namely, London, Edinburgh, Glasgow, Birmingham, and Leeds." Dalton considered Proust's law of definite proportions and concluded that chemical compounds are formed by the combination of certain unit weights of the elements. The smallest possible unit he termed an atom, following Lucretius; and he concluded that the atoms of the elements must vary in weight, these atomic weights being basic physical properties of the elements.

Jöns Berzelius was the organizer of the science of chemistry. He was a medical man, teacher, and finally a professor of chemistry at the College of Medicine at Stockholm. He introduced the system of chemical nomenclature, of the symbols for the elements and formulae for compounds, and he developed great skill in chemical analysis, as a result of which he determined the atomic weights of the elements with such precision that his determinations were not superseded for many years.

The analytical work in which Berzelius displayed such surpassing skill could, of course, determine only the combining equivalents of the atoms. The assumptions made by various chemists as to the number of atoms which combine to form a compound resulted in different values for the atomic weight. If, as it was easiest to believe, one atom of hydrogen combined with one atom of oxygen to form water, the atomic weight of oxygen was 8. The solution of the difficulty could have been found in the hypothesis of Amadeo Avogadro, professor of physics at Turin, who introduced the idea of the *molecule* as the smallest part of a substance which can exist free in a gas and postulated that equal volumes of gases under the same conditions contain the same number of molecules. Unfortunately, however, although this theory was published by Avogadro in 1811, it was nearly fifty years before its importance was generally recognized and the problem of the atomic weights of the elements was solved in its present form.

As chemists became more and more interested in the study of the innumerable compounds of carbon, they began to devote their attention to the production of new substances, that is, to synthesis. Throughout the second half of the nineteenth century, the main advances in chemistry were in the synthesis of new carbon compounds, in the field which is now known as *organic chemistry*.

In the rise of organic chemistry, the greatest influence was exerted by Justus von Liebig, professor of chemistry at Giessen, who not only contributed much to the science by his own studies but also was the teacher of the great school of organic chemists that flourished in Germany in the nineteenth century. In 1836, A. W. von Hofmann, for instance, entered the University of Giessen with the intention of studying law, but under von Liebig's influence he changed his field of work to chemistry, in which he became one of the great discoverers in the field of organic chemistry. In

1845, Hofmann became professor of chemistry in the newly founded Royal College of Science in London. One of his students, W. H. Perkin, as a boy of seventeen discovered the first synthetic dye. In 1864 Hofmann went to the University of Berlin as professor of chemistry, and in his laboratory were trained many of the chemists who established the German dye industry.

In the early days of organic synthesis, the structure of the compounds produced was very difficult to understand. In 1835, Friedrich Wöhler, then teaching at Cassel, wrote to Berzelius, under whom he had studied: "Organic chemistry just now is enough to drive one mad. It gives me the impression of a primeval tropical forest, full of the most remarkable things, a monstrous and boundless thicket, with no way of escape, into which one may well dread to enter."

We can easily understand this feeling of Wöhler's. The increase in the number of the compounds of carbon, which have since shown such amazing proliferation, naturally appalled chemists accustomed to think in terms of the simpler inorganic chemistry. The difficulty, of course, was that through the "forest" of which Wöhler wrote there was no path blazed. No one had mapped a system of organic chemistry. The beginning of the making of this path was the work of von Liebig and Wöhler. Unlike as the two were, von Liebig was justified when he wrote to Wöhler: "When we are dead, the bonds which united us in life will always hold us together in the memory of men as a not frequent example of two men who loyally, without envy or malice, contended and strove in the same domain and yet remained closely united in friendship."

The key to the understanding of organic compounds came with the idea that certain groups of atoms are to be found in many compounds of cognate structure. Thus, if ethyl alcohol and ethyl chloride are analyzed and their compositions written, they will be represented as $C_2 H_6 O$ and $C_2 H_5 Cl$. Their relationship becomes much clearer if we write these formulae as $C_2 H_5 OH$ and $C_2 H_5 Cl$, from which we see that they both contain the group $C_2 H_5$, which is known as the *radical* ethyl. The importance of these radicals was first realized as a result of the work of von Liebig and Wöhler on the compounds derived from benzoic acid that contain the radical benzoyl, $C_6 H_5 CO$. Jean Dumas and P. Boullay had even earlier recognized the existence of the ethylene radical, and Bunsen found the cacodyl radical in the organic compounds of arsenic, which he investigated. Berzelius, who at this time was the recognized leader in chemical science, had formulated the structure of inorganic salts as depending upon the union of two electrically opposed components, these being the oxide of the metal and of the metalloid. Berzelius applied this same idea to the structure of organic compounds, formulating ethyl chloride as directly analogous to sodium chloride. The great generalization of Berzelius was later to be revived in the theory of electrolytic dissociation. But it does not apply to organic compounds, and its advocacy by Berzelius undoubtedly delayed the advance of organic chemistry for a number of years. The opposition to Berzelius centered around two ideas. Von Liebig believed that the properties of organic compounds depended upon the presence of *radicals,* so that ethyl chloride was cognate with ethyl alcohol, since both of them contain the radical ethyl, rather than with sodium chloride. Dumas, on the other hand, classified organic compounds into *types.* Thus he found that the progressive substitution of chlorine for hydrogen atoms in acetic acid left the type of compound undisturbed. Monochloroacetic acid, dichloro-, and trichloroacetic acid are all acetic acids. The idea of types was extended by A. W. Williamson, the predecessor of Ramsay at University College, London. He considered alcohols, ethers, and acids to belong to the water type of compounds; whereas A. Laurent and C. F. Gerhardt regarded the amines as of the ammonia type.

All this work was leading to the clarification of the structure of organic compounds, but our present structural formulae we owe primarily to August Kekulé and A. S.

Couper. Kekulé wrote a most dramatic description of his discovery. He was on a visit to London. He wrote:

> I sank into a reverie. The atoms flitted about before my eyes. I had always seen them in movement, these little beings, but I had never succeeded in interpreting the manner of their movement. That day I saw how two small ones often joined into a little pair; how a larger took hold of two smaller, and a still larger clasped three or even four of the small ones, and how all span round in a whirling round-dance. I saw how the larger ones formed a row and only at the end of the chain smaller ones trailed along. The cry of the conductor, "Clapham Road," woke me up from my reverie, but I occupied part of the night in putting at least sketches of these dream-products on paper. Thus originated the structure-theory.

While the molecules of a very large group of compounds, the aliphatic compounds, could be built up as chains of carbon atoms, it was not possible to formulate in a similar manner the aromatic compounds, which are characterized by a relatively high proportion of carbon and never contain less that six carbon atoms in the molecule. The simplest member of this group is the hydrocarbon benzene. Benzene, first isolated by Faraday, is shown by analysis to have the composition C_6H_6. Since carbon atoms have a valency of four, a compound with the composition C_6H_6 should be highly unsaturated, reactive, and unstable. The compound C_2H_2, acetylene, is, indeed, very unsaturated, reactive, and unstable, as is evident when its structural formula $HC\equiv CH$ is considered, for the two carbon atoms are attached to each other by three bonds and can therefore add two atoms each without dissociating. But benzene is not unstable or reactive; it is stable and rather inert.

In 1865, Kekulé, then professor of chemistry at Ghent, was engaged one evening in writing his textbook. "But it did not go well; my spirit was with other things. I turned the chair to the fireplace and sank into a half-sleep. Again the atoms flitted before my eyes." His imaginative eye, sharpened by repeated visions of a similar kind, could by this time distinguish large structures of complicated construction. He had seen rows of atoms linked together, but never yet rings; nor had anyone else. This is how the idea came to him: "Long rows, variously, more closely, united; all in movement, wriggling and turning like snakes. And see, what was that? One of the snakes seized its own tail and the image whirled scornfully before my eyes. As though from a flash of lightning I awoke." *

But the picture Kekulé had seen of the snake that had seized its own tail gave him the clue to the most puzzling of molecular structures, the structure of the benzene molecule. For it Kekulé suggested a closed ring of six carbon atoms, to each of which a hydrogen atom is attached:

$$
\begin{array}{c}
H \\
C \\
HC \quad\quad CH \\
| \quad\quad\quad | \\
HC \quad\quad CH \\
C \\
H
\end{array}
$$

This formula interpreted the behavior of benzene and its derivatives in a satisfactory manner. For instance, it explained the fact that when two hydrogen atoms in benzene are substituted by other atoms or radicals, three different *di-substituted* compounds can be obtained. Kekulé pointed out that these could depend on the position of the two substituted atoms in the ring. When they were next to each other, they could be called *ortho;* opposite to each other, *para;* and in the position where they were separated by one hydrogen, he used the term *meta* compounds:

$$
\begin{array}{ccc}
\begin{array}{c}
X \\
C \\
HC \quad CX \\
| \quad\quad | \\
HC \quad CH \\
C \\
H
\end{array}
&
\begin{array}{c}
X \\
C \\
HC \quad CH \\
| \quad\quad | \\
HC \quad CX \\
C \\
H
\end{array}
&
\begin{array}{c}
X \\
C \\
HC \quad CH \\
| \quad\quad | \\
HC \quad CH \\
C \\
X
\end{array}
\\
\text{Ortho} & \text{Meta} & \text{Para}
\end{array}
$$

* John R. Baker, *Scientific Life,* p. 13, London, Allen and Unwin, 1942.

It was Kekulé's pupil W. Koerner who gave the experimental proof of this relation. He made the three isomeric dibrombenzenes and the mononitro compounds derived from them; and he found that the number of mononitro compounds derived from each dibromo compound was that which would be prophesied by the Kekulé formula, and thus he identified the position of the bromine atoms in the different dibromo derivatives.

These theories of molecular constitution supplied the chemists with the map and compass by which they could penetrate that tangled forest of organic chemistry. They could understand the difference between structural *isomers;* that is, compounds of identical composition and molecular weight but different chemical behavior. The first of these isomers had been discovered by Wöhler and von Liebig in the pair cyanic acid and fulminic acid. Such isomerism was now understood as being caused by a different linking of the atoms in the molecule. A little later it became possible to distinguish between isomers that differed only as the left hand differs from the right. The organic chemists soon evolved methods by which they could determine the position of different groups in the molecule and could build molecules according to plan.

As early as 1849, E. Frankland had been able to synthesize hydrocarbons of the methane series. If, for instance, ethyl iodide was heated with zinc, zinc iodide was formed, and the two ethyl groups united to form butane. Frankland, indeed, discovered the zinc alkyls and used them in synthetic operations, an early suggestion of the most important Grignard reaction, in which magnesium is employed instead of zinc.

In 1877, C. Friedel and J. M. Crafts at the Sorbonne discovered the reaction that is known by their names. In it, alkyl groups can be introduced by treating a compound such as benzene with an alkyl chloride in the presence of anhydrous aluminum chloride. About the same period also, the value of the reactive methylene group was recognized, and syntheses built on compounds containing it became of general importance in organic chemistry. These synthetic methods were satisfactory to the organic chemists as long as they were dealing with the compounds derived from benzene or from the heterocyclic ring structures, which, to some extent, simulate the properties of benzene; that is, as long as organic chemistry used as its base materials the oils derived from coal tar. But after the first World War, the great oil-refining and chemical companies of the United States started to study the possibility of using petroleum products as the base for new groups of organic compounds, and the attention of the manufacturing chemists became concentrated on the aliphatic organic compounds, those composed of chains of carbon atoms and derived from acetylene, natural gas, or the decomposition products of petroleum. With these compounds, it was found that reactions could be produced in the gas phase with great facility, using catalysts that might be solids, liquids, or even gases. As a result, the classical aliphatic chemistry ceased to have any relation to manufacturing processes.

The standard method of preparing acetic anhydride, for example, is by the treatment of acetyl chloride with sodium acetate. The process for manufacturing acetic anhydride, which is used on a large scale, however, bears little relation to that classical reaction. In that process, acetic acid is catalytically decomposed in the gas phase at a very high temperature to ketene (CH_2CO), the inner anhydride of acetic acid; and the ketene then reacts with the molecules of acetic acid to form acetic anhydride. More and more reactions of this type are taking the place of the classic organic syntheses and are making available large quantities of substances that used to be chemical curiosities.

Many of these new chemicals have a double bond in their structure; that is, two carbon atoms are united not by one but by two bonds. These compounds polymerize easily because one of the bonds is sufficient to hold the carbon atoms together, while the other can supply a connection to link the

molecules of the substance together to form chains or net-
works of molecules, producing compounds having high molecular weights. Such compounds have long been known in
nature; molecules of sugar, for instance, polymerize to form
starch and cellulose. By this means, chemists have built up
a large group of so-called *plastics*—compounds having a high
molecular weight and usually valuable properties comparable
with those of the natural products that have been of such
value to man throughout the ages, such as wood, wool, cotton,
and glass. The study of the plastics and of high-molecular
compounds generally is now a very important branch of
chemistry, and the ideas involved in the structure of polymers
are coming to the front in modern chemical theory.

The chemical reactions that occur in living organisms have
been studied primarily by chemical physiologists, and the
determination of the nature of some of the simpler of these
reactions will be discussed in the next chapter (page 169).
The identification of some of the compounds formed and
their synthesis in the laboratory have, however, been among
the triumphs of organic chemistry, which, indeed, owes its
very name to this field of work. The nitrogen-containing
compound urea was identified by von Liebig in the blood and
urine of mammals, in which it is the chief vehicle for the
elimination of the nitrogen produced by the katabolism of
the proteins. In 1828 Wöhler synthesized urea, an event
that aroused great interest and some controversy since urea
had been considered a typical product of "vital" processes.
After von Liebig, the greatest name in this field of chemistry
is Emil Fischer, who, after acting as assistant to Adolf von
Baeyer at Munich, became professor of chemistry successively
at Erlangen, Würzburg, and Berlin. While studying derivatives of hydrazine, he discovered that phenylhydrazine reacts
with sugars to form well-crystallized compounds, *osazones*.
Then he turned his attention to nitrogen-containing compounds related to uric acid and showed that all of them
were derived from a base, purine, which he synthesized, with
many of its derivatives. Then he returned to the study of

the sugars and synthesized many of them, identifying and, in many cases, preparing the stereoisomeric forms. The difficulties produced by fermentation in this work turned Fischer's attention to the chemical ferments and enzymes, in regard to which he and his coworker, E. Abderhalden, laid the foundations of our present knowledge.

From the sugars and ferments Fischer transferred his attention to the proteins. He succeeded in breaking down these complex products of vital metabolism into amino acids and other nitrogenous compounds, solving their constitution and synthesizing them. He was thus able to prepare in the laboratory polypeptides analogous to the natural proteins.

Other fields of the chemical study of naturally occurring substances relate to the plant alkaloids, which are of great pharmaceutical interest, and to the coloring matters of plants. Perhaps the most striking examples of this field of chemistry are the recent determinations of the structure of the vitamins and the hormones derived from the ductless glands. The industrial production of synthetic vitamin C (ascorbic acid) and especially of vitamin B_1 (thiamin) provides an adequate supply of these necessary materials.

The properties of the compounds of carbon and their production by synthesis are the field of *organic chemistry*. On the other hand, the study of chemical reactions and of the equilibria produced in those reactions is the field of *physical chemistry*.

It had long been known that the progress of a chemical reaction is influenced by the amounts of the reacting substances, but it was not until 1850 that the progress of a reaction was measured and the results expressed as a mathematical equation. This was done by L. Wilhelmy at Heidelberg, who showed that when cane sugar was inverted by acids, a reaction which can be followed with the polariscope, the amount of cane sugar inverted in a unit time is proportional to the amount of sugar present. Just at that time, the attention of chemists was largely directed to the discussion concerning the structure of organic compounds, and it was twelve years before the study of reaction velocities was resumed. Then, in 1867, the full significance and generality of the problem were recognized by two Norwegian scientists, C. M. Guldberg and P. Waage. They stated that the velocity of a reaction at constant temperature is proportional to the product of the active masses of the reacting substances, this being the fundamental law of chemical kinetics, which is generally called the *law of mass action*.

With the discovery of this principle, many chemists turned their attention to the velocity of reactions, which soon centered upon the phenomenon of *catalysis*. This term had been introduced by Berzelius for reactions the velocity of which was greatly increased by the presence of small amounts of foreign substances that apparently took no part in the reaction and underwent no change. The conversion of starch into sugar, for instance, is accelerated by dilute acids. Hydrogen peroxide decomposes rapidly in the presence of finely divided platinum, which also assists the oxidation of ethyl alcohol to acetic acid. Berzelius said: "I don't believe that this is a force quite independent of the electrochemical affinities of matter, but since we cannot see the reaction and mutual dependence, it will be more convenient to designate the force by a separate name." That name was *catalysis*.

We have seen that Wilhelmy discovered the laws of chemical kinetics in the study of the inversion of cane sugar, which was catalyzed by acids. It was at Wilhelm Ostwald's laboratory at Leipzig, sixty years after the work of Berzelius, that the study of catalytic phenomena was systematically brought into the domain of chemical kinetics and investigated quantitatively. Ostwald founded the greatest school of physical chemistry and brought together the work of Guldberg and Waage, of Willard Gibbs, J. H. van't Hoff, Svante Arrhenius, and W. Nernst in his great textbook of general chemistry, which, with the *Zeitschrift für physikalische Chemie,* supplied the written sources through which physical chemistry could be taught to the student.

Just as the work of Guldberg and Waage supplied the key

to the study of reactions in homogeneous systems, the *phase rule* of Willard Gibbs opened the door to the effective analysis of heterogeneous systems in which the reacting substances are present in more than one phase—as solids and liquids, for instance. Willard Gibbs published his work in the transactions of the Connecticut Academy. Because of this rather obscure place of publication and the mathematical form in which it was developed, chemists were slow to recognize its value. It was not until Ostwald published his translation of Gibbs' papers in 1891 and H. W. B. Roozeboom, at the beginning of the twentieth century, studied heterogeneous equilibria on the basis of Gibbs' phase rule that it became generally known to chemists and physicists as a principle of the highest value in the classification of heterogeneous equilibria.

In a general way, it may be stated that the effect of changing temperature, pressure, or concentration in any heterogeneous system would have to be considered a special problem for each system investigated were it not for the phase rule. In any system, we have *components*—such as salt, water, and acid; *phases*—gaseous, liquid, and perhaps several solid phases; and variables—such as temperature, pressure, and concentration, which are known as *degrees of freedom*. The phase rule, which states that the degree of freedom of the system is equal to the number of components plus two minus the number of phases present, enables any well-defined system to be classified and analyzed without difficulty. This rule has been of the greatest importance in many practical applications of chemistry, and, in particular, chemical engineering has made great use of it. All phenomena of precipitation, evaporation, separation of salts, and compositions of alloys are interpreted by Gibbs' phase rule. The great rise of industrial chemistry around 1900 was largely conditioned by this chemical idea, which had remained in incubation for so long a period between the time when it was conceived by Gibbs and the time when it was generally adopted.

In the years between Gibbs' writing and the application of

his work, the physical chemists developed another great chemical idea, the theory of electrolytic dissociation, first advanced by the Swedish chemist Svante Arrhenius. Arrhenius' theory arose from the application of the gas laws to chemical solutions by the Dutch chemist van't Hoff. Just as the pressure of a gas is a measure of the concentration of the gas molecules, so the osmotic pressure of a solution, which is the pressure produced through a semi-permeable membrane that transmits the solvent but not the molecules of the material dissolved, is a measure of the concentration and, thus, of the molecular weight of the substances present. In dilute solutions of salts this principle, which held beautifully for solutions of sugar, failed until Arrhenius introduced the conception that salts in solution dissociated into unit particles that were oppositely charged electrically. Faraday had already postulated such charged particles to explain the conduction of an electric current through a solution and had termed them *ions*.

It is now recognized that the simple picture developed by Arrhenius is not adequate to account quantitatively for the behavior of solutions of electrolytes, although his fundamental concept of dissociation is still the basis of the modern theories of Peter Debye, E. Huckel, J. N. Bronsted, and others. Today we do not consider the behavior of the single ion, but the potential forces of the whole system of ions, in which each is acted upon by the electrostatic field created by the others. From such considerations, we can calculate with reasonable accuracy many of the thermodynamic properties of solutions, and can predict something of salt and ion effects as related to rates of reactions.

As the chemical elements were identified and their atomic weights were determined, it became possible to discern a sort of order in their properties. They could be classified into families whose chemical properties were similar. Thus, there are the alkali metals, the alkaline earths, the halogens, and so on. The compounds of sulfur resemble those of oxygen far more closely than they do those of nitrogen, which, however, are akin to those of phosphorus. As a result of similar considerations, D. I. Mendeleev, professor of chemistry at St. Petersburg, was led to classify the elements by plotting properties which could be measured quantitatively, such as the atomic volumes, against the atomic weights. The curves showed that the same properties repeated periodically, and Mendeleev classified the elements in what is known as the *periodic table*. By extrapolating this table, he was able to prophesy the existence of elements that had not yet been discovered and to state their approximate properties. Several of these prophesies were justified by the discovery of the elements that he had foreseen.

In the last years of the nineteenth century, two discoveries were made that disclosed the existence of elements for which there seemed to be no room in the periodic table. The first was the discovery by Sir William Ramsay of the rare gases of the atmosphere. In 1882 Lord Rayleigh started to redetermine the density of oxygen and hydrogen and later extended the work to nitrogen, whose atomic weight is of fundamental importance in connection with the determination of the atomic weights of many elements. He used nitrogen prepared from the atmosphere by the elimination of the oxygen and of all other reactive gases, such as carbon dioxide and water vapor, and also nitrogen prepared by the decomposition of ammonia. To his astonishment, the atmospheric nitrogen was appreciably heavier than that prepared chemically. After many checks, he discussed the matter in 1894 with Ramsay, who investigated the nature of the atmospheric nitrogen by causing it to react with metals, such as magnesium, which combine with nitrogen. About one per cent of the gas would not react, and this proved to be a new gas having a higher density than nitrogen and a different spectrum. Moreover, this new gas would not react with anything at all, for which reason it was named argon, the "lazy" gas. Following this discovery, Ramsay succeeded in isolating four other gases having properties similar to argon—helium,*

* Chapter V, p. 116.

neon, krypton, and xenon. For a little time it looked as if there were no place for them in the periodic table, and then it was realized that they formed a new group of elements of zero valency unable to form compounds. Instead of casting doubt on the classification, they extended and enhanced its validity.

An even more important discovery of hitherto unknown elements was made when Pierre Curie and his wife isolated from the residues of uranium ore the strongly radioactive radium, of which the atoms were found to be decomposing and changing into atoms of lower atomic weight. Stimulated by Roentgen's discovery of the x-rays in 1895, a number of observers tested various fluorescent materials under the impression that the origin of the x-rays might be connected with the fluorescence that the cathode stream excited in the glass. Among these observers, Henri Becquerel used some beautiful yellow-green crystals of uranium salts and found that when these were wrapped in black paper and left in contact with a photographic film, they produced a blackening of the film when it was developed. This observation excited a good deal of interest. Madame Curie and her husband studied salts of other elements and discovered that thorium would also produce an effect on a film in the same way that uranium did and that the activity of different thorium and uranium ores differed, some of them producing four or five times as much effect as another ore containing the same amount of metal. The tests finally indicated that the natural uranium ore known as *pitchblende* contains something highly active. Monsieur and Madame Curie undertook to analyze systematically about a ton of pitchblende ore, testing all the products at each step for their activity as shown in the production of ionization in an electroscope, an effect that proved to be parallel to the exposure of a photographic plate. This resulted in the isolation of two residues, in one of which the barium of the pitchblende was isolated and in the other, the bismuth; these residues were forty to sixty times more active than uranium. However, normal barium and bismuth showed no activity, so that it was concluded that these residues contained substances originally in the pitchblende that were chemically very similar to barium and to bismuth. These substances could be isolated by a long tedious process of fractional crystallization, and when it was carried out, new elements were identified chemically. The one associated with the barium was named *radium,* and to the one found with bismuth Madame Curie gave the name *polonium,* from her own country, Poland.

If the scientific world had been startled by the discovery of the x-rays and the identification of the electron, this discovery was even more astonishing. Here for the first time were chemical elements that were obviously unstable. The radium salts were visibly decomposing. In the process of decomposition, they emitted (1) beta rays, that is, electrons; (2) gamma rays, which were soon shown to be x-rays; and (3) a new radiation of short penetrating power but of great intensity, to which the name *alpha rays* was given. These rays, when studied in a magnetic and an electric field, proved to be streams of positively charged particles. The relation of their mass to their charge showed that they had a mass either twice that of hydrogen, that is, they had an atomic weight of 2, or they were atoms of helium that had a weight of 4 but carried two positive charges. Sir Ernest Rutherford, whose name now comes into the story, showed that the particles were, indeed, doubly charged atoms of helium and that they turned into helium by picking up negative electric charges by collision with hydrogen atoms, the helium being identified by the bright yellow line with which it glows and which can be seen in the spectroscope.

The successive transformations of radium and polonium were followed by chemists and physicists. It was shown that radium changes into several solids successively, and then into a gas, which, in turn, changes into a solid and then into another solid, and so on until, finally, the changes cease and a stable atom of lead is produced. In this process, a series of radiations are emitted—sometimes alpha rays, sometimes the beta rays or electrons, and almost always some of the gamma or x-rays. Uranium has an atomic weight of 238. It passes through five transformations in becoming radium, which has an atomic weight of 225; and the radium passes through nine transformations before becoming lead with an atomic weight of 206, the last element before lead being polonium. Thorium, in the same way, goes through a series of transformations before the atom stabilizes as an atom of lead, with an atomic weight, however, not of 206 but of approximately 208.

H. G. J. Moseley, a young student working with Rutherford at Liverpool in 1913, measured the wave lengths of the x-rays emitted by various elements when they were used as the anti-cathode in an x-ray tube; that is, when the stream of electrons falling upon them in the tube produced x-ray emission. Using Rutherford's picture of the atom, Moseley was able to show that the frequency of the x-radiation is proportional to the square of the number of the element, the number being the position of the element in the list of all known elements; that is, the number of hydrogen, the lightest element, is 1; that of helium, 2; of lithium, 3; and so on. This discovery enabled Moseley to assign the numbers to all the elements and thus to show what elements were missing from the list, the numbers of the known elements being related to their chemical properties by the periodic classification. When it was realized, after the work of Rutherford and Bohr, that an atom consisted of a positively charged nucleus surrounded by electrons traveling in orbits, the total charge of which was equal to that of the nucleus (Chapter V, p. 111), it became clear that the chemical properties of the atom depend upon the electrons in the outermost orbit. From the periodic classification, it was realized that the innermost orbit can contain at most two electrons, that the next two orbits may contain eight each, and then the orbits contain eighteen electrons, and so on. The number of electrons in the atoms of each element can be stated definitely and corresponds to Moseley's atomic number.

The structure of the chemical elements, therefore, the charge on the nucleus, which is the same as that of the atomic number, and the number of electrons were all worked out. One difficulty still remained, however. The atomic weights of the elements are not the same as their atomic numbers. The atomic weight, for instance, of helium is 4; its atomic number is only 2; and it has only 2 electrons. If the hydrogen nucleus, which is generally called a *proton,* has a weight of 1, helium might be expected to have 2 protons in its nucleus, which would give it two positive charges. Having 2 electrons, it would be neutral, and its atomic weight should be 2. The problem was solved when James Chadwick—like Moseley and Aston, one of Rutherford's collaborators—found that, under some circumstances, from atoms exposed to radiation, particles could be obtained having a mass equal to that of the proton but no electric charge. They are called *neutrons,* and they represent the missing units in the structure of the nucleus of the atom. The helium nucleus, for instance, contains 2 protons and also 2 neutrons, these supplying the necessary units of weight to account for the atomic weight of the element as a whole.

The discovery of the neutron made possible an explanation of the nature of the isotopes, discovered by Aston. The chemical properties of an element depend upon the number of its electrons, and the nucleus must have a number of protons equal to the electrons to maintain electric balance in the atom as a whole. The number of neutrons in an atom, however, do not affect the chemical properties, so that it is possible to have two atoms with the same number of electrons, the same atomic number, and the same chemical properties, but a different total mass, because of a difference in the number of neutrons present in the nucleus. Thus, in the case of the two isotopes of neon that Aston discovered in the mass spectrograph, the particles in the rays had different masses. The neon with an atomic weight of 20 has in its nucleus 10 protons and 10 neutrons; its atomic number is 10, and it has 10 electrons; but the neon with an atomic weight of 22 has the same structure as regards protons and electrons but has 12 neutrons instead of 10. It differs from its twin only by being slightly heavier, which makes it possible to achieve a separation in the mass spectrograph.

The most interesting isotopic element discovered is the isotope of hydrogen, which has an atomic weight of 2. It was isolated by Harold Urey at Columbia University in 1931 after its existence had been predicted by R. Birge and D. Menzel at the University of California to explain the difference between the chemical atomic weight of hydrogen, which represents, of course, the average weight of the atoms of the mixed isotopes, and the atomic weight as determined in the mass spectrograph, which shows only the weight of the proton itself. This isotope of hydrogen has twice the atomic weight of hydrogen, since the neutron weighs as much as the proton, and it is consequently not very difficult to separate it from ordinary hydrogen. Moreover, the difference in weight is sufficient to make it behave somewhat differently from hydrogen itself. The hydrogen isotope has even been dignified by a separate name, deuterium.

As a result of the clarification of atomic structure, chemists were able to make a new attack on the nature of the valence bond. The valence bonds of Kekulé and Couper were represented by a line drawn between the symbols of two chemical elements, indicating that the elements were connected in some way, but the nature of the bond was completely unknown. Indeed, its nature could not possibly be known before something was known of the structure of the atoms.

In 1916 G. N. Lewis worked out the electron theory of valence, in which he emphasized the stability of the group of 8 electrons in the case of the lighter atoms. If the outer ring contains exactly 8 electrons, the element has zero valence; that is, it is one of the rare gases and is incapable of forming molecules or compounds. When the outer electron ring of the element contains less than 8 electrons, it can form compounds in which the electron ring of the one element is completed by electrons from another element, making 8 electrons in all. On the basis of this theory, Lewis and Irving Langmuir were able to explain the structures of many chemical compounds; and the Lewis model of the nature of valency has been generally accepted. One difficulty in this explanation, however, is that the electrons, depicted by Lewis as part of the structure of the atoms, were bound in position, whereas in the Rutherford-Bohr atoms, the electrons were free to revolve in their orbits. In fact, the atom as pictured by the physicists has never been entirely reconcilable with the properties required by the chemists for their atoms. Recently, however, the mathematical physicists appear to have found the solution for such difficulties.* By the application of quantum mechanics, it seems that the orbital atom may provide the necessary mechanism for the formation of the electronic bonds required for the stability of compounds.

Recent developments in nuclear physics have accelerated the synthesis of chemistry and physics into one subject. We have seen that the nuclei of the atoms are known to consist of protons and neutrons, the total number corresponding to the atomic weight of the element, whereas the number of protons gives the atomic number. The atoms of nearly all the elements are stable; only the few radioactive elements disintegrate of their own accord. These radioactive elements, however, give out a great deal of energy when their atoms disintegrate. The total energy given out by a pound of radium in a year would convert nearly a ton of water into steam, although it would take twenty-five hundred years for half the radium to disintegrate. The radioactive elements, therefore, indicate that an enormous amount of energy is available if the nuclei of the atoms can be made to disintegrate.

Experiments by Rutherford and his associates showed that this disintegration could be accomplished when the nuclei were struck by particles of very great energy, such as the alpha rays from radium. The breakdown of nitrogen atoms by

* Chapter V, p. 113.

Rutherford in 1919 by these charged alpha particles was the first example of the artificial disintegration of atomic nuclei.

The next problem for the physicists was to produce artificially accelerated particles that would disintegrate nuclei instead of using the alpha particles naturally emitted from radioactive atoms. Attention was therefore turned to the production of very high voltages, by which beams of electrons and heavier particles, such as charged protons or deuterons—the nuclei of deuterium—could be accelerated. By the use of large induction machines or high-voltage transformers and valve tubes, it was found possible to obtain electric pressures of the order of millions of volts. An important step was taken by E. O. Lawrence, who invented the cyclotron. In it, a beam of atomic nuclei started at a comparatively low voltage is accelerated by an alternating electric field as the particles travel in a spiral orbit produced by a magnetic field. As they swing around the circle, they are continually exposed to acceleration and travel faster and faster until finally they escape as a very rapidly moving beam of atomic nuclei. The nuclei generally used are those of hydrogen and helium and, especially, deuterium.

Using hydrogen nuclei (protons) produced in an electric discharge and accelerated to high velocity by means of applied voltage, J. D. Cockroft and E. T. S. Walton in 1932 found that they could produce helium nuclei by the combination of protons with lithium nuclei. If we write this out as an equation, and insert the weights of the particles involved, we get the following:

$$\text{Li} \quad + \quad \text{H} \quad = \quad 2\text{He}$$
$$7.0182 \qquad 1.0081 \qquad 8.0080 \; [+ \; .0183]$$

Thus in this reaction the transformation of the lithium and hydrogen nuclei into two helium nuclei leaves a surplus of mass; and, since no other particles of matter are produced, this mass must be converted into energy. The experiment showed, indeed, that large amounts of energy were produced in the form of radiation. We can calculate the amount of energy produced from Einstein's equation (Chapter V, p. 115), stating that the energy produced, in ergs, is the change of mass, in grams, multiplied by the square of the velocity of light, which has the tremendous value of 9×10^{20}. When atoms are disintegrated in this way, enormous amounts of energy are released. No effective energy could be obtained from such experiments, however, because only a very few of the charged protons are captured by the lithium nuclei, and so much energy is required to produce the beam of charged protons that the procedure is quite hopeless as a means of producing useful energy.

What is needed is a nuclear reaction that would be self-propagating. When a piece of paper is lighted, only a small portion burns initially, but the flame spreads until all the paper is consumed. To get energy from the atom, an atom is required that in disintegrating produces particles that will disintegrate the next atoms they meet. In 1939 some experiments showed that such a self-propagating reaction was possible for one of the uranium isotopes. There are several isotopes of uranium; the common one has an atomic weight of 238. It is radioactive and disintegrates very slowly indeed to form the radium series of elements. Another isotope of uranium has an atomic weight of 235 and occurs to the extent of 0.7 per cent, or about 14 pounds per ton of uranium. This isotope is disintegrated by the impact of neutrons, but it does not disintegrate by simply emitting one or two particles. The atom actually splits in two, forming two new elements that are first radioactive and then turn into stable elements. This process is known as *fission,* and when such a catastrophe happens to an atom, a number of neutrons are emitted. In the case of *uranium 235,* as it is called, a neutron starts the reaction, and then it is propagated by the neutrons produced by fission. For this reaction to be propagated through a mass, a certain quantity of 235 is required. Otherwise, so many neutrons escape from the outside into the air that not enough are available to keep the disintegration going throughout the mass. Also, the 235 must be fairly pure.

If too much of the common isotope of uranium, the 238 isotope, is present, the neutrons will be absorbed by the atoms of 238 and will not be available to disintegrate the 235.

The production of the atomic bombs that were dropped on Japan depended on the working out of these problems on an engineering scale. The uranium 235 was separated from ordinary uranium by very laborious processes that produced only a very small amount in each piece of apparatus, but by building enormously large factories enough of the isotope could be obtained for effective use in bombs. At the same time, a new element, *plutonium,* was produced, this material being made by the exposure of uranium 238 to neutrons supplied from uranium 235, the whole reaction taking place in a structure called a *pile.*

Plutonium was first made in a cyclotron. A neutron adds uranium to an atom of 238 to produce an unstable uranium isotope, which emits an electron from its nucleus and turns into a new element, number 93; and this in its turn emits an electron and turns into plutonium, element 94. Plutonium is similar in its radioactive properties to uranium 235. Chemically, of course, it differs from uranium and can be separated from it by chemical means. Plutonium in sufficient quantity undergoes a self-propagating fission like uranium 235, so that atomic bombs can be made either by the use of the uranium isotope 235 or by the use of plutonium produced from uranium in a pile.

Chapter VII

THE GROWTH OF BIOLOGICAL IDEAS *

The sciences did not develop in a logical order. Without previous advances in the physical sciences, biology could make only limited progress. It was, however, one of the first sciences to which serious study was devoted; whereas chemistry, as we have seen (page 119), made very little advance until toward the end of the eighteenth century. Twenty-two centuries before, in the fourth century B.C., Aristotle had already made considerable progress in the investigation of animal life. He was an acute natural historian with a particular interest in the study of reproduction and development. In the following centuries biology continued to be studied and taught in the museum at Alexandria. The store of biological knowledge continued to grow until the time of Galen, in the second century after Christ. Galen studied in Alexandria and his native Asia Minor, and later in Rome. He was essentially a medical man, but he made important studies on the anatomy and physiology of various mammals. With his death the helix of history had completed a revolution, and biology sank back into insignificance.

It is true that knowledge of the work of Aristotle and Galen was kept just alive during the long period of the Dark Ages, but there was little or no progress. When the study of the ancient authors was revived, they came to be regarded as

* The reader who requires a textbook treatment of the history of biology should use one or more of the following standard works:

W. A. Locy, *Biology and Its Makers,* New York, Henry Holt, 1915.

E. Nordenskiöld, *The History of Biology,* London, Kegan Paul, 1929.

C. Singer, *A Short History of Biology,* Oxford, Clarendon Press, 1931.

authoritative and not open to correction. It is not easy nowadays to understand the spirit of those times, when biologists were not expected to discover new facts, but only to expound and illustrate the old opinions. Progress demanded not a revival of the ancient knowledge but a breaking down of the belief in the infallibility of the writers of antiquity. When at last this tradition was broken, largely through the initiative of the anatomist and physiologist Andreas Vesalius (page 77), new knowledge of living organisms came rapidly; so rapidly, indeed, that the old knowledge was soon of relatively small importance, and it can scarcely be regarded as the basis of modern biology. For this reason the biology of antiquity, despite its considerable intrinsic interest, deserves only a passing mention in a short history.

Modern biology may be said to have originated about 1537, when Vesalius left his native Belgium, settled in the University of Padua, and began to become influential. From then onward progress has been more or less continuous. Nevertheless, it is convenient to divide the history of modern biology into earlier and later periods; and 1838 is a convenient year from which to date the later period. The first decades of the nineteenth century were a time of steady advance in several departments of biology. In 1838 this steady advance was suddenly followed by spectacular discoveries. The cell theory, enunciated by Schleiden in 1838, led to an outburst of cytological research; and the study of the minute structure of organisms received a second great stimulus from the re-introduction of the staining technique about a decade later. Then in the fifties came the first understanding of the alternation of generations in plants, and Darwin's and Wallace's theory of evolution by natural selection. All these advances, following one another in rapid succession, make it reasonable to date the later period of modern biology from the year 1838. Our history will therefore be related in two sections, the first covering the three centuries that started in 1537, and the second dealing with the rapid advances that have occurred in many branches of biology between 1838 and the present day.

The rebirth of biology, then, started about 1537 in the fields of human anatomy and physiology. Although Vesalius' factual additions to knowledge were considerable, his main service to science was to dare openly to doubt the authority of the ancient writers. Greater discoveries than his were made by others. Andrea Cesalpino, a man of extraordinarily diverse interests in science, technology, and philosophy, described the circulation of the blood in 1593 but, unfortunately, failed to give particulars of the way he got his knowledge. It was left to the Englishman, William Harvey, to put the physiology of the circulation on a really sound basis. His *Exercitatio anatomica de Motu Cordis et Sanguinis* is deservedly one of the classics of science. He not only described the path of the circulation but also made quantitative studies of the amount of blood pumped by the heart. Knowledge of human anatomy progressed rapidly, and by 1664 the Oxford professor Thomas Willis had described the external form of the brain and cranial nerves of man so accurately that little of major importance has been added to his account. People had come at last also to understand that glands are synthetic organs that pour out their secretions through ducts.

The object of Vesalius, Willis, and most of the other early anatomists and physiologists was practical. They wished to improve the art of medicine. Before biology as a whole could flourish, it was necessary that the true spirit of science should develop, that the study of nature should be undertaken as an end in itself. A number of people were studying and classifying plants during the sixteenth century, but they were doing so mainly because they wished to identify the species that provided drugs and other substances of material value to man. So long as this was so, real progress in botany could not be made. The first person to treat the subject as an independent science, without regard to practical applications, was the versatile Cesalpino; and when he died in 1603, the stage was set for rapid developments in this science.

Kaspar Bauhin of Basle made a fairly natural classification of the higher plants, using the idea of genera and species, though without giving them names. That was at the beginning of the century; toward its close Bachmann of Leipzig (or Rivinus, as he called himself) suggested that no plant name should contain more than two words. Half way through the eighteenth century the great Swedish natural historian Linnaeus applied Bachmann's suggestion to both the plant and animal kingdoms, founding the universally accepted principles of the nomenclature of organisms. His classification of larger groups, however, was defective. It was not until near the end of the century that the first real attempt to classify plants on a natural system was made by Antoine de Jussieu, a member of the celebrated French family of biologists of that surname.

The first fairly satisfactory classification of the animal kingdom was made by that great comparative anatomist Georges Cuvier in his *Le Règne Animal* (1816). Cuvier divided all animals into four groups: the Vertebrata, Mollusca, Articulata, and Radiata. With the true mollusks he classified three lots of organisms (the lampshells or "brachiopods," the sea squirts and their allies, and the barnacles), which subsequent research showed to be unrelated both to the mollusks and to each other. The Articulata, again, have had to be dismembered into two separate *phyla,* or main divisions of the animal kingdom, the Annelida and Arthropoda. His Radiata was not a natural group. It contained eight major phyla of the animal kingdom and some lesser groups, the affinities of which are still obscure.

Cuvier did much to increase knowledge of fossil animals. The study of paleontology had begun long before. In 1669 that versatile Dane, Nils Steensen—Catholic priest and human anatomist of the first rank—recognized the organic origin of fossils and concluded that the rocks in which they occur had been laid down as sediment in water. Although he could not know it, he thus originated that branch of knowledge in which the theory of evolution would one day find its firmest basis. De Buffon, an imposing figure of eighteenth century science, considered that a certain amount of change occurred in the form of organisms with the passage of time, but he did not formulate any systematic theory or explain the causes. Near the end of the century Immanuel Kant, the great philosopher, allowed the possibility of evolution in his *Critique of Judgment,* and Charles Darwin's grandfather was already a firm believer in the gradual adaptation of organisms to their needs through the inheritance of what were later to be called *acquired characters.* So also was the brilliant though speculative Lamarck, although his ideas on the subject did not attract a lot of attention at the time. More important than any of these for the firm foundation of the theory of evolution was a clergyman and economist named Thomas Malthus. He was not himself a student of evolution or even of biology; he was interested in the pressure of human population on the available means of subsistence. But his writings on the subject were later to influence both Charles Darwin and Alfred Russel Wallace, whose theory of evolution was to have such a profound effect on biological thought sixty years later.

Modern ideas on evolution are closely bound up with our knowledge of heredity, but in the eighteenth century that subject was illuminated by only a single glimmer of light. Just the very beginnings of knowledge were visible in Joseph Koelreuter's experiments on hybridization. But no one then could guess what wonders Mendel and his successors would do with the numerical analysis of results in this field. Koelreuter made a start along a line that did not begin to influence thought on the causes of adaptation until long after the main battle for evolution had been fought and won.

Understanding of the processes of reproduction came very slowly. A Dutch student, Hamm, discovered spermatozoa in 1679. In the next century Spallanzani filtered semen and showed that fertilization cannot take place unless spermatozoa are present in it; but he did not conclude that they were the actual fertilizing bodies. Reproduction could not be seriously investigated until it was known for certain whether organisms arise only from pre-existent organisms or whether, on the contrary, they are sometimes spontaneously generated from non-living matter. Harvey himself in 1651 announced that every organism originates from an egg (though he never saw the egg of mammals); and ten years later Redi, physician at the court of Florence, showed experimentally that larvae appear in rotting meat only if flies lay eggs on it. That remarkable man John Needham, an English Catholic priest living on the continent, performed experiments nearly a century afterward that caused him to be a firm believer in spontaneous generation. Toward the end of the eighteenth century Spallanzani boiled various organic materials in airtight containers and showed that life did not originate in them. His experiments were so carefully done that they might have settled the matter, but, as we shall see (page 166), the subject was raised again much later. The Mammalian egg was first seen in 1827 by the Esthonian K. E. von Baer, who also made marvelously exact studies of the development of various animals and may be regarded as the father of modern descriptive embryology.

It is not only from eggs, however, that animals arise. This had been shown toward the middle of the eighteenth century by a Genevese naturalist, Abraham Trembley, who was acting as tutor in a family living near The Hague. Trembley observed some remarkable *polyps* in water taken from a ditch and studied them with such profundity that his work is quoted in modern textbooks not as a historical curiosity but for its sound information on an important subject. He was the first to show that certain animals can be multiplied artificially by cutting them into pieces, and he made a careful study of the processes of regeneration. His friend Lyonet, a Frenchman living at The Hague, made equally exact studies in a different field. His description of the anatomy of the goat-moth caterpillar is an example of accuracy and careful observation that is thought by many good judges never to have been surpassed to this day, although others before him—especially that unhappy Dutchman, Jan Swammerdam—had done magnificent work on insect anatomy. Such men as these show how wrong it is to adopt a cynical or contemptuous attitude toward the biologists of the seventeenth and eighteenth centuries.

Trembley made a marvelously detailed study of the natural budding of his little fresh-water polyp, *Hydra*. He showed how a small part of the body wall protrudes, develops new parts, and becomes a new individual, which separates. His work on this subject actually proved that there is a real *epigenesis* or increase in complexity during development. But he was influenced so much by the belief of his friend and compatriot Charles Bonnet in *preformation* that he never relinquished belief in it. Bonnet had shown that plant-lice multiply without the intervention of a male parent. He was struck by the high degree of development of the young at birth and knew that in many insects each stage of development is enclosed within the skin of the previous stage. He generalized from these facts and imagined that each generation of organisms was folded up in a minute form within the reproductive bodies of the previous generation. Development, then, was only an unfolding, not a real increase in complexity. Extending this idea still further, he imagined that *all* subsequent generations were already folded up within the first female of each species that existed on the earth. This *emboîtement* of generation within generation was widely believed during the eighteenth century. Although Trembley's observations were sufficient to disprove it, it was the writings of the placid Caspar Wolff that at last made people reject preformation and accept epigenesis. Working first at Halle and later in St. Petersburg, Wolff showed that there is a genuine increase in complexity in the development of both plants and animals and not a mere unfolding of preformed parts. His work was scarcely noticed until the beginning of the nineteenth century, after his death. Wolff paved the way for von Baer and other great descriptive embryologists of the nineteenth century.

Scarcely anything was known about the function or significance of flowers until toward the end of the seventeenth century, when people at last began to realize that the stamens and pollen could be regarded as male and the style, ovary, and ovule as female. This knowledge came from the work of the English medical practitioner Nehemiah Grew and the Tübingen professor, Camerarius. The latter removed the male flowers of plants in which the sexes are borne separately and found that fruit was not set. It was in the sixties of the eighteenth century that the professional botanist Koelreuter first showed clearly that certain plants are pollinated by the wind and others by insects. At the end of the century the hermit-like Christian Sprengel made a wonderfully exact study of insect pollination and the devices by which plants escape self-fertilization.

Understanding of the significance of leaves came later than that of flowers. In the first half of the seventeenth century the mystical chemist van Helmont had made one very concrete observation: a willow watered only with rain water gained 159 pounds, while the soil contained in the bowl in which it grew lost only three ounces in dry weight. No one followed up this observation until in 1727 Stephen Hales, a Middlesex clergyman, published a work of genius called *Vegetable Staticks,* in which he showed that plants absorb air through their leaves and that part of their substance is derived from the air so absorbed. This work marked the origin of knowledge about the nutritive function of leaves. Hales also measured the transpiration of water through plants and studied root pressure.

In the second half of the eighteenth century the Unitarian clergyman Joseph Priestley showed that air that had been "injured" by the burning of candles could be made suitable for animal respiration by keeping green plants in it; in fact, green plants give off the gas that we now call *oxygen.* Jan Ingenhousz, a Dutch doctor, showed in 1779 that plants only give off "dephlogisticated air" in sunlight; in darkness, on the contrary, they produce the gas that we call *carbon dioxide*. These discoveries were not fully understood at the time. We now know, of course, that green plants take up carbon dioxide from the air through their leaves and under the influence of sunlight build the carbon into the substance of their tissues. In both light and dark they use oxygen and produce carbon dioxide in respiring, just as animals do, but it is only in darkness that the carbon dioxide is passed out into the air, for it cannot then be used as a source of nourishment. It was not until the beginning of the nineteenth century that the Swiss investigator Nicolas de Saussure put the subject of plant respiration and nutrition on a firm basis by means of quantitative studies.

Meanwhile something was being learned about the respiration of animals. Up to the middle of the seventeenth century no one had the slightest idea why one must breathe to live; respiration was not in the least understood. In 1660 Robert Boyle, the famous chemist, showed that mice and sparrows die in partial vacua. Eight years later a more fundamental discovery was announced by John Mayow, the lawyer and Oxford don (though Boyle was probably partly responsible for it). It was shown that it is not air as a whole, but something in air, that is necessary for life. Mayow called that something *igneo-aerial* particles; it was, of course, oxygen. Nearly a century then elapsed without further discoveries being made on this momentous subject. At last Joseph Black, professor of chemistry at Glasgow, showed that "fixed air" (carbon dioxide) is a product both of combustion and of respiration. Not long afterward a young Scottish medical man Daniel Rutherford showed that "fixed air" is not the only irrespirable matter in air; but he missed the actual discovery of nitrogen. It was in 1780 that the fundamental discovery about respiration was made by the famous French scientists Lavoisier and Laplace: "Respiration is therefore a combustion, slow it is true, but otherwise perfectly similar to the combustion of charcoal." They had realized that both burning and respiration are examples of oxidation. The old Italian biologist Spallanzani corrected their one big error not long before he died at the end of the century: the combustion does not occur in the lungs, as Lavoisier and Laplace had thought, but in the various tissues of the body.

The cell theory was first foreshadowed in the seventeenth century. The English microscopist Robert Hooke described the *cellulae* of cork; the Italian Marcello Malpighi, the *ultriculae* of various plants; and Nehemiah Grew, their *cells* or *bladders*. The Dutch petty official Anton van Leeuwenhoek frequently figured cells. He also discovered blood corpuscles and saw the nuclei of those of fishes, but the time was not ripe for an understanding of the fact that both plants and animals *consist* of cells. The follow-up of these seventeenth century discoveries was slow. Half way through the eighteenth century Caspar Wolff, the epigenesist, held that both plants and animals consist of *ampullae*, but rigid proof was lacking and the science of cytology had yet to be born. At the beginning of the nineteenth century a Frenchman, Mirbel, maintained that the cell is the basis of all structure in plants. That extraordinary and erratic genius Lorenz Oken, amid a maze of fantastic writings, claimed that all organic beings—not plants alone—originate from and consist of *little bladders*.

About the same time advances were made in other branches of what we should now call *histology* and *cytology*. The young Professor M. F. X. Bichat—he was to die almost at once, at the age of thirty—was making the first comprehensive classification of the tissues of the human body, strangely enough, without using the microscope. In 1825 a much-overlooked French scientist, F. V. Raspail, introduced the use of iodine into microscopical studies to show the distribution of starch in tissues by its intense blue reaction. He thus founded the science of *histochemistry,* and went on to devise tests for other substances occurring in plant and animal tissues.

From about 1830 onward cytology progressed rapidly, as though in anticipation of the events of 1838. The versatile

Scottish botanist Robert Brown (as eminent in plant geography as in microscopical studies) recognized the nucleus as a regular feature in plant cells. It had already been named in 1823, but the universality of its occurrence had never been realized. Attention had been focused on the cell wall, a mere lifeless box, and not on the living substance within. The most obvious object in the living substance within the box is the spherical or oval nucleus, and it is perhaps not strange that the nucleus attracted attention before the substance in which it was embedded. Now at last the substance itself was studied, by the French zoologist Félix Dujardin, who called it *sarcode*. His description of it was remarkably accurate. "I propose to give this name," he wrote, "to what others have called a living jelly—this viscous, transparent substance, insoluble in water, contracting into globular masses, attaching itself to dissecting needles and allowing itself to be drawn out like mucus; occurring in all the lower animals interposed between the other elements of structure." We could hardly do better today in so few words, though nowadays we have numerical data for viscosity and elasticity, and we should not restrict the substance to the lower animals. Dujardin's word, however, did not stick. The Czech investigator Johannes Purkinje introduced *protoplasm,* and this caught on some years afterward when the great cytologist Hugo von Mohl of Tübingen applied it to the same substance in plants.

Purkinje did something a good deal more important than introduce a useful new word. He pointed out that the skin of animals, especially embryos, consists of cellulae like those forming the connective substance or *parenchyma* of plants. The stage was now set for the enunciation of the cell theory.

It was in October 1838 that the ex-lawyer M. J. Schleiden and the anatomist Theodor Schwann dined together in Berlin. They were a strangely assorted pair. The volatile Schleiden, having shot himself in the forehead and recovered, can have had little in common with the placid Schwann apart from their intense interest in the minute anatomy of organisms. Schleiden described to Schwann the nucleus of plant cells, and Schwann at once recognized it as corresponding to something with which he was familiar in cells of the spinal cord of Vertebrates. The two men repaired forthwith to Schwann's laboratory in the Anatomical Institute of the University. Schwann showed his friend the cells of the spinal cord, and Schleiden at once recognized the nuclei as corresponding to those with which he was familiar in plants. Due recognition must be given to the researches of those who had preceded them in cytological investigations, but this occasion may nevertheless be justly regarded as marking the first general formulation of the cell theory. The two men published separately. They made big mistakes, but the *cell theory*—the theory that plants and animals simply *consist* of cells and the products of cells—must properly be ascribed to them.

Throughout the forties discoveries followed one another quickly. Mohl came to regard cell division as the usual means of production of new cells. The Swiss zoologist von Kölliker showed that spermatozoa are cells, not mere parasites in semen. His friend and compatriot Karl Nägeli witnessed nuclear division and was the first to glimpse the chromosomes. It was these two friends, more than anyone else, who established one of the profoundest truths in biology: that the egg is itself a cell and gives rise to the cells of the new individual by repeated division. (It is true that Schwann had already regarded the egg as a cell, but he did not understand how new cells arise.) It was not until the fifties, however, that it became generally accepted that cells never arise except from pre-existing cells, and not until the sixties that protoplasm was called "the physical basis of life," and the cell "a lump of nucleated protoplasm."

Much was being learned, then, about the minute *structure* of animals; something also about the *physical properties* of protoplasm; and its *chemistry* was not being neglected. Friedrich Wöhler, the distinguished German chemist, had already synthesized urea from inorganic components in 1828 and thus shown that there was no sharp distinction between organic and inorganic compounds. Raspail was making advances by applying chemical color tests to thin sections of plant and animal tissues, and the word *protein* was coined. Just at the end of the forties, however, a striking technical advance was made, which greatly encouraged the study of structure while turning attention away from the study of substance. This was the rediscovery of staining. Dyes had been used sporadically in biological microtechnique a long time before, but the biologists of the day did not know this. One after another they began to rediscover what had been forgotten and to apply it very much more actively than it had ever been applied. The different constituents of tissues and cells have extraordinarily different affinities for different dyes; and by a little experimenting one can soon learn to make one part of the cell stain in one color and another part in another. One of the great difficulties in studying protoplasm had been its transparency. That difficulty was now removed at a stroke, and a clear insight was given into the minute structure of organisms.

Dyes, unfortunately, tell us little about chemical composition, and the study of substance soon became overshadowed by that of structure. Raspail's work with real chemical tests was overlooked, and microscopists began to become amateur dyers. Then came Darwin with his *Origin of Species;* and morphology—the study of form—received a second powerful stimulus. People began to think that the main purpose of biology was to exhibit the evolutionary relationships of organisms, and that could be done by the study of structure, without much attention being paid to substance or function.

In recent years there has been a healthy tendency to revert to the study of substance instead of concentrating exclusively on structure. All sorts of interesting methods have been used to find out more about the actual substances of which cells are composed. Some of these methods are actually new; others are revivals of very old ones. One of them, micro-incineration, actually originated with Raspail in the eighteen twenties but has only recently been developed. Thin slices of plant and animal tissue are heated in an oven until all the organic matter is burned away and only inorganic ash is left. The process is so carefully carried out, however, that the ash remains exactly where it was, and the microscope reveals the exact location of the inorganic constituents within individual cells.

America has led the world in originating and developing novel methods for investigating the substances of which the cell is composed. Professor R. R. Bensley of Chicago, youthful despite his years, has been and still is a pioneer in this work. It was he who first showed how the minute components of cells can be separated from one another by passing tissues through fine sieves and then centrifuging the material at carefully regulated speeds. In this way some of the most elusive cell constituents, previously only peered at under the highest powers of the microscope, have been obtained in masses that one can hold in one's hand. Instead of having to rely on conjecture as to their composition, one can now subject the material to direct chemical analysis.

But we must return to the outburst of discovery in various fields that followed the formulation of the cell theory. The phenomena of reproduction began to be put upon a cellular basis. In 1855, for the first time, the German botanist Nathaniel Pringsheim saw the essential feature in the act of fertilization. As early as 1823 the microscopist Giovanni Amici had observed the tube formed by the pollen grain and seen it enter the ovule. Pringsheim now saw the cellular nature of fertilization. He was working with *Vaucheria,* one of the lowly plants that form masses of branching green threads in our ponds and ditches. He found that two cells, the active male spermatozoid and the female ovum or egg, *fuse together* to form a single cell and that the single cell grows and differentiates until it becomes a new plant individual. Spermatozoa had been known since the seventeenth century and the corresponding spermatozoids of ferns since the forties, and it seems rather surprising that an understanding of the general principles of fertilization came so slowly.

It was not until the seventies that the Swiss scientist Hermann Fol actually saw the spermatozoon of the starfish enter the egg and thus showed for animals, as Pringsheim had shown for plants, that fertilization consists of the fusion of two cells.

Meanwhile, the fundamental principles of the reproduction of plants were at last being discovered. A considerable obstacle had to be overcome before progress could be made in this subject. It had been supposed, quite naturally, that the ovule was to a plant what the egg is to an animal. It was an amateur botanist who made all the fundamental discoveries that exposed the falsity of this view. Early in the fifties Wilhelm Hofmeister, a music-seller, showed that mosses and ferns exhibit an alternation of generations: that the spore of a fern plant does not grow into another fern but into a completely different kind of plant, which itself reproduces sexually to produce the fern plant once more. That was remarkable enough, but Hofmeister went straight on to show that there is an exactly comparable alternation of generations in the flowering plants: part of the ovule is actually another generation living parasitically on the parent that produced it. This was one of the most important botanical discoveries ever made, and it was all the more noteworthy because Hofmeister did his work at a time when the actual process of fertilization was not understood in either plants or animals. Hofmeister, who was self-taught and had had no academic training, now became a professor of botany at a great German university.

Attention now began to be focused on nuclei. When nuclear division occurs, chromosomes become apparent. Chromosomes are colorless and transparent, but they have an intense affinity for many ordinary dyes. Indeed, it is for that reason that they are called by a name that means color bodies. They had been glimpsed by Karl Nägeli early in the forties; now, owing to the rediscovery of staining, they had become one of the easiest things in the cell to study. In the seventies the German botanist Eduard Strasburger made out the principal features of nuclear division in plants, and shortly afterward the process was found to be essentially the same in animals. Each chromosome divides longitudinally at cell division, and of the two halves one goes into each daughter cell to help reconstitute a new nucleus. About the same time the German biologist Oscar Hertwig made the momentous discovery that the essential feature of fertilization is the fusion of two *nuclei,* one derived from each parent. It was in the eighties that the Belgian zoologist Edouard van Beneden made one of the most fundamental discoveries of cell science: each nucleus in the body contains two *packs* of a definite number of chromosomes, the number being constant throughout all the cells of the body in each species, *except the spermatozoon and egg,* which have only one pack each. The significance of fertilization now began to become apparent; it brought two packs together again.

People were not slow to see that the extraordinarily precise behavior of the chromosomes must indicate some function of significance for life; and it was suggested that they were connected with heredity. So they are, and the knowledge that would have proved it was already lying on the dusty shelves of the libraries of Europe. But no one read the necessary paper. An almost unknown Austrian biologist, the monk Gregor Mendel, had written it in 1866. It had been published in an obscure journal and sent to London and elsewhere; but scarcely anyone paid any attention. His paper was independently rediscovered in 1900 by three scientists in different parts of Europe; and it was at once realized that a very important discovery had been made, so important, indeed, that the study of heredity is to this day often called Mendelism.

Mendel worked mainly with edible peas, which he grew in the garden of his monastery. His experiments were novel in that he crossed plants differing in one or a few sharply contrasting characters; and these he followed through, generation by generation, always counting accurately the number of plants showing each character. It was particularly his analysis of the ratios in which the characters reappear that brought him posthumous fame. He showed that the *genes,* as we now call the units responsible for heredity, do not interfere with one another when they come together at fertilization. A hybrid inheriting genes for both tallness and dwarfness does not have genes for medium size in its germ cells: on the contrary, each of its offspring inherits from it only tallness *or* dwarfness. When Mendel's paper was discovered, it was quickly shown that his *laws* of inheritance, as they came to be called, were not something peculiar to the edible pea but were of universal application to plants and animals, including man.

The paper was discovered in 1900, and two years later a fact of first-rate importance was pointed out by W. S. Sutton of Columbia University. The way in which the chromosomes are distributed from parent to offspring was known. Sutton pointed out that it was exactly the same as the way in which the genes are distributed, according to Mendel's findings. Mendel had died in 1894, a few years before van Beneden had made his discoveries. Had he lived those few years, Mendel might perhaps have forestalled Sutton. But the last years of his life were so much occupied with the financial affairs of his monastery that it is unlikely that he kept in touch with chromosome research.

It was already known in 1901 that the sexes differed slightly in their chromosome complement, and it was not long before people realized that chromosomes are not only the bearers of the genes for ordinary characters, but also the determinants of sex. A few years later an American biologist began studying inheritance in a little fly rather similar to the housefly but smaller, called *Drosophila.* This animal presents extraordinary advantages for the study of heredity. It can easily be kept in large numbers in the laboratory, the reproductive cycle from one generation to the next is very short, and the chromosomes are few. It has taught us more about heredity than any other organism. A group of workers centered around T. H. Morgan at Columbia University began to make marvelous discoveries. It had been known for some time that certain genes behave under certain circumstances as though they were linked to others in heredity. Soon it became apparent that the number of groups of linked genes is the same as the number of different chromosomes (only four in each cell, in *Drosophila*). Morgan and his collaborators were soon able to say which chromosome was concerned with the inheritance of which group of linked genes and, further, *in what order* the genes were arranged along each chromosome. They could say that at this point on a given chromosome was the gene that expresses itself most obviously by its effect on the shape of the wings; here, farther along the same chromosome, another affecting the size of the legs; farther again, a gene affecting body color; and farther still, one affecting the size of the wings; and so on for hundreds of other genes.

The evidence for the arrangement of the genes in a certain order along the chromosomes was entirely indirect. The chromosomes looked more or less the same all along their length; there were no little marks that might actually be the genes. The complicated indirect evidence was obtained, like Mendel's, from the counting of the numbers of individuals showing various inherited characters in each generation, not from a minute study of the chromosomes themselves. It was not until the nineteen thirties that final ocular proof of the chromosome theory of heredity was obtained. It became known that some curious objects in certain cells of *Drosophila* and other flies were nothing but gigantic chromosomes, about one hundred times as long as normal ones. They are like tapes with stainable marks across them. These marks are something like the divisions on a measuring tape but differ in that some are thick and some thin; and these thick and thin marks follow one another in a regular order. That regular order is the same in very nearly all the corresponding chromosomes in the cells of all the flies of the same species,— very nearly, but not quite—and the exception gave the clue to a most important discovery. A few peculiar specimens of *Drosophila* were known, in which the ordinary indirect evidence suggested very strongly that some of the genes, corresponding to a short length of one chromosome, were the "wrong" way around. It occurred to T. S. Painter and his associates at the University of Texas to look at the giant chromosomes of these particular specimens. In his microscope he saw for the first time concrete proof of the chromosome theory of heredity: the thick and thin marks were in fact arranged the wrong way around in part of the chromosome concerned.

Our modern understanding of heredity has thrown a strong light on the causes of evolution without, as yet, providing an explanation that commands general assent. Back in 1858 a theory of causes had been put forward by Charles Darwin and Alfred Russel Wallace. The idea had occurred to them independently. Both had read Malthus on population (page 148). In Darwin's mind the idea formed gradually over a long period of years; into Wallace's it flashed suddenly while he was suffering from an attack of malaria in the East Indies. They saw that organisms produce far more offspring than can survive; that those offspring differ among themselves; and that, on the average, those that chance to be the best adapted to their environment will survive. These fittest individuals would pass on their characters to their offspring, and thus the race would gradually evolve. The publication of *The Origin of Species* in 1859 is a landmark in the history of biology.

Nowadays we can see that Darwin's chief service to science was the production of a mass of evidence that evolution has occurred. That mass of evidence has been multiplying ever since, and the fact of evolution is not today in doubt. But although he studied variation and wrote a large book on it, Darwin never found out how variations are inherited. It was Mendel who did that. It is interesting to speculate on what would have happened if Mendel had sent a copy of his paper to Darwin. The latter, however, died without ever hearing of Mendel's work, and real study of the causes of evolution was delayed until after the product of the monastery had been brought into the light of day in 1900.

The geographic distribution of organisms, their habitats, foods, and "enemies" seem relatively simple matters for study, and one might have looked for the development of these branches of biology early in the history of science. It is true that Linnaeus and other eighteenth century biologists recorded the habitats of the plants they described, and Captain Cook took biologists with him on his great voyages of exploration; but no serious attempt was made to draw general conclusions or to found a special branch of biology covering the natural conditions of life of plants and animals. It was not until 1858 that an ornithologist, P. L. Sclater, made an attempt to divide the world into zoological regions. The theory of evolution then gave an impetus to such studies. It was necessary to find not only what organisms lived where, but how that particular distribution had come about in the course of geological time. In the seventies Alfred Russel Wallace, himself a great traveler, rounded off his general contribution to the theory of evolution by a particular study of geographic distribution. His zoological regions, founded for the most part on those of Sclater, have retained much of their validity to the present day. *Wallace's line,* which he drew with such remarkable accuracy through the map of the East Indian archipelago, still separates the extraordinary fauna of the Australasian region from the animals of eastern Asia.

The study of the home life of organisms or *ecology,* as it eventually came to be called, still remained in a primitive state. Darwin himself was a first-rate ecologist, as every reader of *The Origin of Species* must know. Academic biologists, however, continued to leave the subject alone, as though mere natural history were beneath their notice. Not sufficient attention was paid to the fact that plants and animals have their particular structure and functions simply because their ancestors lived in certain habitats, were subject to the rigors of certain climates, fed on certain foods, and were liable to attack by certain other organisms. It was indefensible to make detailed studies of structure and function while neglecting the environmental factors in response to which the structure and function evolved, but ecology is only now coming into its own.   Old-fashioned natural history is becoming strictly scientific.   The habitats of organisms are coming to be described not in vague terms, but in the form of accurate numerical data for the temperature and humidity of the atmosphere, the intensity of the visible and ultraviolet light, and so forth.   The complex interrelations of organisms are also being disentangled.   It has been shown that there are regular cycles in the abundance and scarcity of many species, though we do not yet understand the underlying causes.   It is very unfortunate that ecological studies have come so late in history; for man has acted like a vandal in destroying the natural habitats in which organisms evolved. In Great Britain only a few small patches of virgin country remain.   Through his radical transformation of his own habitat, man has disturbed that of most terrestrial organisms.   He himself has become an environmental factor in the lives of plants and animals comparable in importance with the natural phenomena of temperature, humidity, mountain-building, and the rest.   It is a pity that he did not start studying ecology before he nearly destroyed the natural subject matter of this branch of biology.   The ecology of the future is likely to be concerned mostly with the relationships of organisms to the artificial environments created by man.

The grand period of biology started and ended with cytological studies.   The year 1838 saw the formulation of the cell theory.   About half a century later the general principles of chromosome behavior were known.   Now, at last, a retrogressive movement had set in.   Darwin's theory led to a concentration of attention on the structure of organisms with a concomitant loss of interest in their substance and functions. People who could have been continuing the scientific study of organisms were indulging in speculation and drawing diagrams from their imagination showing how one group of organisms had been derived from another.   A book was written to show that Vertebrates evolved from king crabs. No limit was set to the free play of the imagination when once the idea of evolution had been accepted. Side by side, however, with much that was valueless—and often curiously intermingled with it—went a profound study of the comparative anatomy of animals. So complete, indeed, was this study that no problem of major importance was left for solution in the twentieth century.

Comparative anatomy alone could not provide insight into the *causes* of evolution. Help came at last from quite an unexpected quarter. It was the rediscovery of Mendelism in 1900 that eventually gave the necessary impetus to studies of evolution. It gradually became apparent that the survival of organisms in the struggle for existence might depend on what Mendelian genes they possessed. Those individuals that had genes determining characters favorable to survival would be automatically selected; the rest would perish and leave few or no offspring. It was seen that in any species a very large set of possible combinations of different genes was available, and on these combinations "natural" or automatic selection would operate: there would be survival of the individuals with the fittest genes. But this was not all; it was found that the genes themselves sometimes undergo sudden changes. The cause of this process of *mutation* is not understood, but it certainly results in the production of new genes; and these behave according to Mendel's rules, generation after generation, until mutation occurs again. Mutation and recombination, then, are thought to provide the material on which Darwin's *natural selection* can act; but our ideas on the causes of evolution must remain hypothetical until we can demonstrate unequivocally the selection of favorable genes under natural conditions of existence.

Although we do not know the causes of natural mutation and are, thus, still ignorant of the real cause of evolution, quite a lot is known about how mutation can be made to occur artificially in the laboratory. In 1927 H. J. Muller, at the University of Texas, discovered that the rate of muta-

tion can be enormously increased by subjecting organisms to
x-rays; and ultraviolet light and radium have since then been
shown to act in the same way. These agencies act on the
chromosomes of the germ cells. We may look for great advances in this line when someone has discovered how to control the process. At present it is a hit-or-miss affair; there
is no known way of producing one new gene rather than
another.

It is strange to recall that the controversy on spontaneous
generation was only laid to rest in the middle of the nineteenth century. We have already seen (page 149) that Spallanzani had disproved spontaneous generation by careful experiments in the sixties of the century before, but people
were not easily convinced. The great Swedish chemist Berzelius (page 121) still believed in the spontaneous generation
of some of the lower animals at the beginning of the nineteenth century; so, later still, did that restless genius of physiology and marine zoology, Johannes Müller. The most
ardent supporter of spontaneous generation, however, was
the Rouen professor Félix Pouchet, who thought that the
fermentation of decaying substances was actually the process
by which the micro-organisms found in such substances originate. This cart-before-the-horse opinion was opposed by
Louis Pasteur, whose critical experiments finally convinced
the scientific world in 1861.

Pasteur went straight on to the study of micro-organisms as
the causes of disease. In 1835 an Italian amateur microscopist, Agostino Bassi, had shown that a disease of silkworms was
caused by a microscopic fungus. Not much attention had
been attracted by this discovery; and now, strangely enough,
Pasteur started his investigation of germs by studying another
disease of the same insect. Things moved quickly in the sixties. Another Frenchman, Casimir Davaine, discovered bacteria in the blood of animals suffering from anthrax and
showed that one-millionth of a drop of infected blood was
sufficient to carry the disease into a previously healthy individual. Pasteur's final proof that micro-organisms are not

spontaneously generated but arise only from pre-existing micro-organisms naturally had a profound influence on the development of bacteriology; for it was at last obvious that exclusion of the germ meant exclusion of the disease. Early in the seventies a German investigator, C. J. Eberth, performed the experiment that linked Davaine's with Pasteur's. He filtered the deadly blood of animals suffering from anthrax and showed that the filtrate was innocuous. There was nothing in the filtered blood that could multiply and cause disease, and the germs could not be generated spontaneously. Bacteriology now made rapid strides, thanks largely to advances in technique. Robert Koch introduced valuable methods for making bacteria readily visible under the microscope by staining them, and he also discovered how to grow them outside the body on jelly in glass vessels, a technique that is still in use today.

Microscopists now looked confidently for the germs of the most diverse diseases; but their confidence was misplaced. It was soon discovered that some diseases could be artificially transmitted from one animal to another, as are diseases caused by germs, despite the fact that no sign of any micro-organism could be detected under the microscope. Pasteur considered that such diseases must be caused by micro-organisms too small for the microscope to resolve. Diseases of this kind were found to occur also in plants. And now, in the last decade of the century, Eberth's filtration experiment was found not to be universally valid. It was shown that the juice of a tobacco plant infected with mosaic disease would cause the same disease in previously healthy plants even if the juice were filtered. Something had been discovered that could only be observed through its effects on organisms; this something had the power of self-multiplication but, unlike ordinary germs, could pass through a filter. This was the starting point of our knowledge of the filter-passing viruses, which are the cause of so many diseases of man, such as smallpox, chicken pox, measles, German measles, influenza, and common colds.

Soon after the turn of the century it was found by P. Rem-
linger in Constantinople that the virus of rabies will pass
through one filter but not through another. This gave the
clue that made it possible to estimate the size of virus particles, although the microscope could not reveal them. Extraordinarily fine filters were made, in which the size of the
holes, though ultramicroscopic, could be determined indi-
rectly. In the twenties virus particles were already known
to be minute. The virus of foot-and-mouth disease is particularly small, not many times larger, in fact, than certain large
molecules, such as the molecule of hemoglobin. A complicated building cannot be constructed from a few bricks, and
it is clear that the viruses must be extremely simple in structure: they seem to stand halfway between living and non-
living matter. We cannot regard them, however, as the
forms in which life first appeared on this planet, for they
seem remarkably dependent on the living cells of organisms,
and they do not multiply in profusion outside the body as
bacteria do. The invention of the electron microscope is
already beginning to help in the elucidation of the nature
of viruses. The resolving power of this new instrument with
suitable objects is much higher than that of the ordinary light
microscope, and actual micrographs of virus particles have
been obtained.

Again and again in the history of science we see new developments foreshadowed in old writings. In 1656 the London
physician Thomas Wharton had claimed that the secretion of
the pineal gland, in the brain, passed into the blood stream;
but no one followed up this idea. It had only recently been
discovered that glands have ducts, and the contrary idea—
that some of them have not—was unattractive. It was not
until the nineteenth century that people began to understand
how hormones or chemical messengers originate in ductless
glands, pass into the blood stream, and exert powerful in-
fluences on the action or growth of distant parts of the body.
In our own times it has been discovered that plants too have
their hormones.

From the thirties of the nineteenth century onward, thanks largely to the work of the great German chemist Justus von Liebig, proteins, fats, carbohydrates, salts, and water were recognized as the main nutritional requirements of man and other animals. So firmly did this idea take root that great independence of mind was necessary in anyone who would doubt it. Yet a Dutchman, G. Grijns, working inconspicuously in the East Indies, did dare to doubt it; he even claimed that men became ill and died just because proteins, fats, carbohydrates, salts, and water were not enough. That was at the very beginning of the present century, and not long afterward the great Cambridge biochemist Sir Frederick Hopkins set the study of vitamins on its feet by critical feeding experiments on animals.

We left the grand problem of respiration on page 153 with Spallanzani's discovery that the reaction of combustible substances with oxygen occurs not in the lungs, as Lavoisier thought, but in the various tissues of the body. This was not definitely proved until the eighteen thirties, and at that time it was still thought that the oxygen traveled from the lungs to the tissues in simple solution in the water of the blood. In the fifties people began to think that it must travel in loose combination with some unknown substance. Today it seems difficult to believe that it was not until the eighteen sixties that this substance was shown to be hemoglobin, the familiar red coloring matter of blood. The discovery was largely due to the investigations of the great German biochemist F. Hoppe-Seyler. Everything seemed straightforward. The oxygen in the air of the lungs combined with the hemoglobin in the red blood corpuscles and was carried in this combined form to the tissues; it then escaped from combination, diffused out of the blood into the cells, and there combined with carbon and hydrogen to form carbon dioxide and water. The energy produced by this combustion was the energy necessary for life.

The form in which oxygen travels in the blood stream had, indeed, been discovered, but the manifold complications of its behavior when it gets to the tissues had not even been glimpsed. In the eighteen eighties C. A. MacMunn brought forward evidence that the tissues themselves, apart from the blood, contain substances resembling hemoglobin. These he named *histohaematin* and *myohaematin*. The great Hoppe-Seyler said that MacMunn's substances were simply decomposition products of the hemoglobin of the blood. MacMunn defended himself: he had shown in his very first paper that his substances were present in the tissues of insects, which have no hemoglobin in their blood. This might have seemed conclusive, but Hoppe-Seyler refused to consider the evidence from insects. He simply printed a note alongside MacMunn's last paper saying that he considered all further discussion of the subject superfluous. People accepted his opinion, and little more was heard of histohaematin, myohaematin, or MacMunn.

It was not until the twenties of the present century that D. Keilin of Cambridge showed that MacMunn had been right and Hoppe-Seyler wrong. It would appear that throughout the plant and animal kingdoms every cell that gets its energy by the ordinary process of combustion contains MacMunn's substances (or *cytochrome,* to use Keilin's word). MacMunn had really been studying something far more fundamental than Hoppe-Seyler. The latter was interested in the vehicle by which oxygen is transported to the tissues in certain animals; MacMunn, on the contrary, was on the verge of discovering what happens to oxygen when it actually gets to cells, whether by Hoppe-Seyler's vehicle or not. We realize nowadays that cell respiration is a matter of enormous complexity. The oxygen by no means simply diffuses into cells and combines with combustible substances. It first combines with cytochrome and is then handed on by this cellular respiratory pigment to combine with the hydrogen of combustible substances, each stage of the process being made possible by the presence of particular intracellular ferments. Knowledge of the processes of cellular respiration is growing rapidly. It is strange to think that if MacMunn had not been crushed by Hoppe-Seyler, we should probably have had this knowledge nearly forty years sooner. A useful lesson can be learned from the sad story: under no circumstances must research be controlled by authority. It is true that Hoppe-Seyler had no legal authority, such as one scientist has over another in a totalitarian state; yet his influence was sufficient to retard by several decades the investigation of one of the most fundamental problems of life.

One cannot guess what branches of biology are going to develop most rapidly in the future, though one can surmise that certain lines have been rather thoroughly worked out and offer poor prospects. Much may be expected from the full incorporation of physiology into biology. In the past animal physiology has been a sort of ancillary branch of medicine, as botany was of pharmacology in the sixteenth century. Plant physiology has never suffered under the same disadvantages; it has developed naturally like the other branches of botany and in concert with them, and is universally regarded as a branch of botany. Zoology, greatly to its detriment, was for long regarded as being concerned with all branches of knowledge of animals *except* that of function. This idea was as detrimental to physiology as to the major subject. A change of outlook is at last manifesting itself. Physiologists have begun to untie the strings that have bound them to man, guinea pig, and frog.

If physiology can break loose from subservience to medicine and stand on its own legs, we may look for rapid progress in our understanding of the processes of growth and differentiation. These are two of the most fundamental phenomena of life. Until now they have been studied mostly by biologists lacking special training in physiology, for professional physiologists have held aloof. Wilhelm Roux, son of a fencing instructor, founded the science of the mechanics of development toward the end of the nineteenth century. The embryological experiments carried out by the philosophic Hans Driesch about the turn of the century led him to conclude that a purely mechanical and chemical explanation of development was impossible.   Then, in the early part of the present century, Hans Spemann of Freiburg was able to localize in early embryos the actual substances that "organize" its further development.   And W. Vogt of Munich, by marking spots with stains on the surface of living embryos, has watched and recorded the complex movements of cells during differentiation.   These men and others have made real progress in investigating the causes that transform a simple egg into a complex adult body, the old problem that Wolff started to attack nearly two centuries ago.   This surely should be a very attractive problem for present-day physiologists, but it is only one among many that await solution by a fully integrated science of biology, in which animal physiology will take its natural place.

Chapter VIII

THE PRODUCTION OF SCIENTIFIC
KNOWLEDGE

We have followed the growth of scientific research from its beginning in the seventeenth century, when the investigators were amateurs engaged primarily in other pursuits but inspired by interest to experiment in the field of natural philosophy. As their knowledge grew, they found a natural home in the universities as professors of natural philosophy. Their welcome in the universities arose from the fact that in the Middle Ages the study of natural phenomena was considered suitable for ecclesiastics, who regarded the knowledge that they derived from their inquiries as a means of developing the fullness of the religious belief both of themselves and of those whom they taught, and who felt that the revelation of the marvels of nature was a fitting part of worship. These ecclesiastics not only studied in their retreats but also taught the more intelligent young men of the day, so that the universities evolved from the institutions of the church.

When the methods of experimental science were developed, the readiness of the universities to accept the responsibility for the advancement of knowledge was due essentially to the fact that the results obtained were immediately applicable to the purpose of teaching. Indeed, only by assiduous effort and discovery could the facts of natural philosophy be sufficiently correlated to make it possible to present them in an orderly manner so that they could be understood by the immature minds with which a university has to deal. This need for investigation by the teacher was so marked and the success of teachers who were engaged in experimental study was so pronounced that it was generally recognized that the best advanced training in science could be obtained only under a man who was himself actively engaged in promoting the science that he taught. Through the nineteenth century, the advancement of science was a function of the work of the universities.

Toward the end of the nineteenth century, the impact of science upon the social life of the western world became evident. Lecturers and writers, such as Tyndall and Huxley, were pointing out to the public that the advances which were occurring in the scale of living arose from the growing knowledge of natural science. And H. G. Wells had a considerable influence upon public thought when he published in 1902 his book entitled *Anticipations of the Reaction of Mechanical and Scientific Progress upon Human Life and Thought.** In this book Wells attempted to analyze the trends of invention and development apparent at the beginning of the twentieth century and to foresee how those new developments might react on the structure of society. It is an excellent book, and, looked at forty years later, it is astonishingly accurate, suggesting that an anticipation of the general course of events over a limited period is not at all impossible, though quite obviously there will be a considerable distortion of the time scale for the different phenomena. Wells, for example, seriously underestimated the rate of development of aircraft. On the other hand, he overestimated apparently the development and influence of the technically trained men.

In the nineteenth century there arose a number of technical industries that depended primarily upon discoveries and inventions made by some individual or group who developed their original discoveries into an industrial process. The history of many industries is that they were originated and developed by a man of genius fully acquainted with the practice of the industry and with such theory as was then known; that his successors failed to keep up with the progress of the industry and with the theory of the cognate sciences; and

* London, Chapman and Hall, Ltd., 1902.

that sooner or later some other genius working on the subject advanced the available knowledge and gave a new spurt to the development of that industry. Thus, in the early days of the technical industries, the development of new processes and methods was often dependent upon some one man, sometimes the owner of the firm which exploited his discoveries. But with the increasing complexity of industry and the parallel increase in the amount of technical and scientific information, necessitating increasing specialization, the work of investigation and development, which had been performed by an individual, was delegated to a special department of the organization, from which arose the modern industrial research laboratories.

The organization of research sections in industry first became of importance in the dye industry in Germany. After the initial discovery of the synthetic dyes by Perkin in England, Hofmann and his students made large numbers of dyes from the oils separated from coal tar, and the students of Hofmann founded manufacturing companies to make the dyes. In this industry, continual research was essential, and very soon groups of chemists were producing a stream of new processes and products, all of them protected as completely as possible by patents. The success of this organization and the expansion of the dye works until they controlled the chemical industry of Germany and a great part of the world inspired others to follow their example.

Certain other industries were founded by scientific men who had made discoveries, and these also engaged in scientific research on a large scale. Research was organized from the very beginning in the telephone companies that Alexander Bell founded, and Elihu Thomson brought the same system into the General Electric Company when it was formed. Soon after the beginning of the twentieth century, therefore, industrial research was firmly established in the German chemical and electrical industries, in the American electrical industry, and, to a small extent, in the British and American chemical industries.

The prototype of another kind of organization for the application of science to industry is the Mellon Institute of the University of Pittsburgh. Laboratories of the type of the Mellon Institute may perhaps be distinguished as technological research institutes, since their work is primarily in technology rather than in pure science.*

At the end of the nineteenth century, the governments of the world started to support a limited amount of scientific research. The oldest government-supported research is that of the observatories, of which the first was Greenwich Observatory, founded in 1675 and supported on a very parsimonious scale by the British government ever since, the head of the institution enjoying the title of Astronomer Royal. During the nineteenth century the federal government of the United States created the Coast and Geodetic Survey, the Naval Observatory, the Department of Agriculture, and the Geological Survey. On the whole, these institutions were devoted primarily to the application of science, although the Bureau of Standards, founded in 1901, and the British National Physical Laboratory, founded in 1899, like the Reichsanstalt, organized by the German government after the Franco-Prussian War, carry out much basic research in physics in addition to their primary task of maintaining the physical standards used in commerce and industry.

At the beginning of the twentieth century, a new factor entered the field of pure science. This was the creation of two privately endowed institutions—the Carnegie Institution in Washington and the Rockefeller Institute. From the fortunes that supplied the funds for them came also the Rockefeller Foundation and the Carnegie Corporation. The great sums available from these sources, no less than the wise judgment of those who administered the sums, have enabled them to make the greatest contributions to the progress of science not only in America but also throughout the world. The Carnegie Institution, particularly, originated a new type of

* Chapter IX, p. 214.

scientific laboratory. The Geophysical Laboratory and the Mount Wilson Observatory are of the convergent type, in which the work of many scientists specializing in diverse fields of science can be concentrated upon certain groups of problems. Such laboratories, which are discussed later under the name of *research institutes*, are likely to be most powerful agencies for the production of scientific knowledge in the future.

One of the most important factors in the organization of scientific research at the present time is the increasing complexity and elaboration of the apparatus used not only in applied science but even in pure science. Research in pure physics in the nineteenth century required a very minimum of equipment, and substantial increases in knowledge were made by workers in small laboratories who spent only a very small sum on apparatus and constructed much of that apparatus with their own hands or with the assistance of a laboratory mechanic. Today the apparatus required for physical research is of the most complex type and requires a great expenditure of money and very well-equipped machine shops. The nuclear physicist, for example, has progressed from the simple apparatus used by J. J. Thomson, Aston, and Rutherford to the cyclotrons invented by Lawrence, of which the largest has cost well over $1,000,000. The cryogenic laboratries, which make large quantities of liquid hydrogen and helium for research at low temperatures, are necessary for much physical research, and the physical phenomena exhibited by the stars are studied with the aid of telescopic equipment involving capital expenditures of millions of dollars.

Again, the identification of coincidences in the frequency differences between spectral lines, which enables the lines to be assigned to different systems in an element, is an extremely laborious operation when performed by hand, and progress in this field of physics was very slow until instruments were designed by which these frequency differences could be analyzed automatically. As a result, the very complicated spectra of a number of the elements have been analyzed within a few years.

In chemistry, the simple laboratories used for analytical work and for the early research in organic chemistry are no longer sufficient for progress in many fields. Work on gas reactions requires very complex equipment. Much chemical work is done at high pressures and much at very high temperatures, and more and more these methods of producing and studying chemical reactions are of importance. Silicate chemistry has involved a complex technology of furnace work.

In certain fields of work, a whole laboratory may be considered a tool. In the advancement of physiology, for instance, a requisite is a synthetic organic laboratory that can prepare the many compounds required. And now it seems likely that physiological research will require a supply of chemicals made with isotopes of the elements or with radioactive isotopes prepared synthetically in the laboratories of nuclear physics.

During a recent discussion of the co-operation that might be effected between industrial research laboratories and the investigators who were studying medicine, it was suggested that what was really required by the medical men was not co-operation but a supply of synthetic chemicals for which they did not have to pay. Experimenters in medicine, as in physiology, require a very large number of synthetic chemicals, the cost of which is far greater than can be met from the usual scanty budget of the investigator. What is needed is a philanthropic organic chemist to make the chemicals that are required; and if progress is to be made in medicine and physiology, this demand must be met. Perhaps one of the most useful things that a philanthropist could do at the present time would be to endow a synthetic organic laboratory to prepare chemicals for use in the medical sciences.

Another tool absolutely necessary in physiological chemistry is the animal colony, and for this to be really effective it will be distinctly expensive both in first cost and in operation. Colonies of selected animals kept under very uniform conditions and supplied with analytically controlled food must be established, and these require much attention and care if the experiments are not to be interrupted by accidental losses from disease. It is necessary, in fact, for us to pay more attention to the health of our experimental animals than we do to our own health. Similar colonies are required for the study of heredity.

The mere accumulation of facts is being expedited very much by improved apparatus. In the study of photography, for instance, much of the fundamental information is obtained in the form of a curve known as the *characteristic curve,* which relates the density of a developed image to the exposure given to the light-sensitive material. To obtain these curves, the material is exposed to a series of light intensities and developed, and then the densities resulting are measured and the curve plotted. With a visual instrument, the measurement of density is a very slow operation, and much effort is required to produce twenty curves in a day. Indeed, such a rate of production cannot be maintained; the making of some four hundred photometric matches in a day is very tiring. Today automatic instruments using photoelectric cells measure the densities and draw the curves, and it is well within the capacity of such an instrument to produce over a thousand curves in a day when used by an unskilled operator. More and more, scientific men are designing improved methods of collecting and analyzing the data on which they can base their studies. Thus they are again accelerating our production of knowledge.

A useful classification of research laboratories in general is based on consideration of whether all the problems investigated are connected with one common subject or are of many kinds having no connecting bond of interest. The first type of laboratory might be called *unipurpose* or *convergent* and the second, *multipurpose* or *divergent.*

In the convergent laboratories, although the actual investigations may cover as great a range of science as those undertaken in a divergent laboratory, all the investigations are directed toward a common end, that is, toward the elucidation of associated problems related to one subject. Thus the staff of the Geophysical Laboratory of the Carnegie Institution, which includes physicists, geologists, crystallographers, mineralogists, and chemists, works on the structure of the rocks and their manner of formation. Although the field of the actual investigations ranges from high-temperature photometry to the study of complex solubility diagrams and their interpretation on thermodynamical principles, the results of all the work carried out are converged on the problem of the structure and formation of the earth's crust. The Nela Park Laboratory of the General Electric Company, in the same way, is studying the production, distribution, and measurement of illumination; and all its work, which may involve psychology, physiology, physics, and chemistry, is related to that one subject.

A laboratory of the convergent type, which carries on work in one field of science for a considerable time, may conveniently be described as a research institute. Research institutes have come into existence in the last half century without our realizing that they represent an innovation in the organization of research, but they will probably be the most important agencies for the production of scientific knowledge in the future. In many cases they have been formed by outstanding investigators at universities. A professor specializes in some field of work and directs the studies of his graduate students into that field. Then others who are interested are attracted to join him until his laboratory is recognized as the natural center for researches on that subject.

Many examples of this process could be given, from which I can take, almost at random, only a few as illustrations. The invention of the cyclotron has made the radiation laboratory at the University of California the central point of the world for research in nuclear physics. At Cambridge University in England, the Cavendish Laboratory has been an institute of physical research under two successive directors, J. J. Thomson, who determined the nature of the electron, and

Sir Ernest Rutherford, who established the foundations of radioactivity. Under men such as these, almost all the work carried on in the laboratory has been concentrated on the subject in which they themselves were working; and instead of teaching general physics, the laboratory is a most valuable and effective research institute. Kamerlingh Onnes established at Leyden a laboratory for research at very low temperatures, where he investigated the superconductivity of metals and the extraordinary properties of liquid helium. Peter Kapitza was so original in his ideas for the study of the physics of very high magnetic fields that the Royal Society fathered for him a special laboratory at Cambridge, and Kapitza is now carrying out similar work in the Soviet Union. In different fields of scientific work, Harlow Shapley at Harvard is concentrating the work of a group upon the properties of the meta-galaxy, and T. H. Morgan in his laboratory at the California Institute of Technology has concentrated on the problems of genetics, especially as exemplified in the *Drosophila* fly (Chapter VII, page 160).

In all these cases, the interest and capacity of a university teacher have supplied the incentive for the organization of a research institute as part of the university structure. Unfortunately, such institutes often languish and die when the teacher himself passes; only rarely can the university find a successor who will justify the continuance of the specialized work. Greater stability is attained when such institutes have been founded deliberately by philanthropic foundations who desired to expend money on the advancement of scientific knowledge. With the present trend toward the use of more and more complicated and expensive apparatus and toward greater specialization in the methods used in investigation, research institutes are becoming more and more necessary for the advancement of knowledge in the future.

At this point it may be well to summarize the various agencies available for the production of scientific knowledge. The basic institution on which everything else depends is the scientific department of the university, and this differs from all other institutions in that it has and should have no direction from outside and complete freedom in its choice of subject. It is from the universities that the bulk of the new ideas by which science is advanced are likely to come, since in all other institutions there is some restriction and will probably always be some restriction in the fields selected for work. The application of science is dealt with primarily in the research laboratories of industry, in the endowed technological institutes, and in the laboratories operated through government departments, which are increasing very rapidly in size and complexity. The more complicated fields of science require for their exploitation research institutes, each of which deals with a limited field of science and is recognized as a center for the advancement of knowledge in that field.

Research institutes will not relieve the universities of their responsibilities for teaching and for conducting scientific research; indeed, the activity of the universities in the prosecution of research may be expected to increase. Whereas the fundamental business of a university is to teach, the argument for research has been that teaching is impossible unless the knowledge is available and that those engaged in the production of knowledge are the best teachers of it. This is undoubtedly true within limits, and it is probable that a research institute is the best training place for a research student. Certainly the graduates from the Cavendish Laboratory would justify the policy of its directors, and a student who had worked under Ramsay would be the first to insist that the eager pursuit of knowledge in that ill-equipped laboratory at University College, London, was a most stimulating atmosphere in which to acquire the methods and habit of research. But for the student who wants a general knowledge of the subject and does not propose to devote himself to research, a too specialized university laboratory has its disadvantages. Moreover, the universities are finding it increasingly difficult to supply the equipment required for research. In the past, the enthusiasm of the investigator, the availability of sympathetic wealthy individuals, and, by no means least, the great philanthropic foundations have, in the end, provided the funds, but at a great sacrifice of time and effort by scientific men.

To a certain extent, the industrial research laboratories will undertake responsibility for special fields of work. The Kodak Research Laboratories in Rochester are, indeed, a research institute devoted to the study of photography (Chapter IX, page 208). But industrial laboratories are fundamentally intended to deal with the application of science rather than with the creation of new knowledge, and it is almost certain that they cannot be expected to provide adequately for the advancement of science on all fronts.

Public taxation is a very important source of the funds needed for the support of scientific research at the present time and one likely to supply the greater part of those funds in the future. In Soviet Russia, with its planned economy, the government has already organized its scientific work in a great group of research institutes distributed throughout the land and controlled, in the last instance, by the members of the Academy of Sciences.* The Academy was founded by Peter the Great. Formerly, its headquarters were in Leningrad, but they have been transferred to Moscow. There are about ninety academicians. In general, each group of institutes is operated by a special committee whose chairman is one of the members of the Academy. Thus, in agricultural science, Professor T. D. Lysenko of the Academy is the president of the Academy of Agricultural Science, which includes altogether thirty members of the Academy of Sciences. Under this operating committee there are throughout the Soviet Union over three hundred institutes of various sizes containing, as a whole, about ten thousand scientists and, in addition, about eight thousand general assistants, field, and laboratory workers. The administrative control of the system is operated separately from the direction of the scientific work.

* J. G. Crowther, *Soviet Science,* London, Kegan Paul, Trench, Trubner & Co., Ltd., 1936.

Similar groups of institutes exist in Russia in all fields of science. A very large organization deals with physics, which is chiefly supported through a division of the government commissariat of heavy industry known as the Scientific Research Sector. Institutes operated by it include the Physico-Technical Institute in Leningrad, directed by Professor Joffe; the Institute of Chemical Physics in Leningrad; the Optical Institute of Leningrad; the Karpov Institute of Physical Chemistry in Moscow; and the Physico-Technical Institute of Kharkov. That in Russia, as elsewhere, institutes are developed to suit the idiosyncrasies of individual scientists is shown by the example of the Institute of Physical Problems.* This institute was organized by Kapitza in 1937 under the control of the Academy to study problems of theoretical physics, especially those relating to the use of low temperatures and strong magnetic fields. In his account of its organization, Kapitza emphasizes his use of a relatively small staff and his practice of following personally the work in the laboratory.

The elaborate organization of science that has developed in the Soviet Union is, of course, of the same pattern as other developments in that country. It is an organized and planned system erected to perform a specific function, and to only a small extent is it the result of organic growth over a number of years.†

The recent proposals put forward by Dr. Vannevar Bush, director of the Office of Scientific Research and Development, in his report to the President of the United States entitled

* A very interesting report on the work of this institute by P. L. Kapitza is published in English in *Voks Bulletin,* No. 9–10, 22 (1943).

† A number of British and American scientists visited Russia on the occasion of the two hundredth anniversary of the founding of the Academy of Sciences. Their reports on the scientific work done there (*Nature,* Sept. 8 and Sept. 15, 1945) show that the actual conduct of work by no means corresponds to the regimented organization suggested in earlier accounts of the system. If we may judge by these reports, the Russian scientific workers control their own work and choose their own problems very much as is done in other countries.

Science, the Endless Frontier, include a new organization for the production of scientific knowledge in the United States. It is to be known as the National Research Foundation. It is intended to make available a considerable amount of money estimated to start at $33,500,000 and to reach $122,500,000 in five years, these sums to be supplied by the federal government from taxation. It is not proposed that the Research Foundation should build, own, or operate laboratories. Instead, continuing the practice of the Office of Scientific Research and Development through the war, programs will be organized and supported in existing laboratories and especially in the universities, and funds will be available for assisting in the training of research workers and in the support of publication. This wide proposal has not yet been implemented by legislation, so that it is too early to judge its effect upon the future organization of scientific research in the United States. The effect should, of course, be very beneficial though there is certainly some danger that the support of scientific research in the universities by an external body might limit the freedom of choice of subject. No doubt this danger will be recognized by the members of the Foundation, and they will do their utmost to guard against it. Nevertheless, the history of science is full of cases where the interests of some scientific worker have been so opposed to the general trend of thought at the time that it would have been quite impossible for him to obtain support for his ideas, and he has been subject to active opposition and ridicule (Chapter VII, page 170).

The most important advances in science will continue to be unexpected, improbable, and even unpalatable, and it is essential that the men who are to make them should not be prevented from doing so. In consideration of this matter, it must not, however, be forgotten that universities at the present time are tending more and more to embark upon industrial research in co-operation with industry, much of this so-called research being really development work of a type calling for energy and inventive ability rather than for scientific imagination. This is likely to be far more disastrous to the free spirit of inquiry in the university than the receipt of support from such an organization as the National Research Foundation.

In Great Britain, as in the United States, the public and the government have been impressed by the great importance of the work done by the scientific men for the prosecution of the war and are considering actively the possibilities of increasing scientific work by the supply of public funds, whose source lies eventually in taxes. There appear to be no proposals in Great Britain for the establishment of research institutes. It is proposed instead to aid the universities and to construct one or more technological institutes of the type of the Mellon Institute, while every effort will be made to encourage research in the laboratories owned by industry and, especially, under the direction of the Research Associations, which are a feature of the organization of research in Great Britain.

In the widespread discussion of scientific research published during recent years, there is little material relating to the actual organization of research laboratories and institutes. It has generally been assumed, in fact, that their organization would be similar to that of a factory or an army. Thus, in 1920, the author of this book wrote: *

> There are two forms of organization. In the departmental system the organization is that familiar to most businesses. The work of the laboratory is classified into several departments; physics, chemistry, engineering, and so on, according to the number necessary to cover the field, and each of these departments has a man of suitable scientific attainments in charge. In a large department each of these men will in turn have assistants responsible for sections of the department, all the heads of departments finally being responsible to the director of the laboratory.
> Under the alternative or cell system the laboratory consists of a number of investigators of approximately equal

* C. E. Kenneth Mees, *The Organization of Industrial Scientific Research*, p. 81, New York, McGraw-Hill Book Co., 1920.

standing in the laboratory, each of them responsible only to the director, and each of them engaged upon some specific research. Each such investigator, of course, may be provided with assistants as may be necessary.

Each of these systems has advantages and disadvantages. Under the departmental system, the advantages are strict organization, good co-operation throughout the departments, a plentiful supply of assistants for the abler men who form the heads of departments or sections of the departments. The chief disadvantage is that the system tends to stifle initiative in the younger men. While it is true that research men require to serve a considerable apprenticeship to older investigators, there comes a time when every man wishes to try to develop his own line of research on his own initiative and to carry out work by himself, and while it is quite possible to provide for such men in a departmental organization, there is some danger that men who are really capable of original work may not get the opportunity to carry it out.

The cell system, on the other hand, provides a good arrangement for men of original initiative and of the self-reliant type; it enables a man to continue a single line of work by himself for a long time and patiently to bring to a conclusion work that in a departmental organization might have been abandoned because of its apparently unremunerative character. On the other hand, the cell system tends to exaggerate the vices of such men. They tend to become secretive, to refuse co-operation, to be even resentful if their work is inquired into; while if a man who has developed a line of work for himself in a cell leaves the laboratory, it may be very difficult for anybody else to take up the work, in which case a great deal of time and money is lost, and work that should have been carried forward is left unfinished. Another objection to the cell system is that men who are good organizers and who are of the type that can carry on work requiring many assistants do not easily find a place in it.

In practice, a balance between these two systems of organization is essential and will develop in any laboratory. It is not possible to work a rigid departmental system, and, on the other hand, no cell system in its most definite form could be effective. The form of organization which is the easiest in administration is undoubtedly some modification of the departmental system, since only by this means can students fresh from college acquire adequate training and at the same time keep in touch with different branches of their subject and avoid the danger of immature specialization.   A laboratory should therefore be organized in departments with an intradepartmental section in which a young man who develops the ability to carry out his own work may be able to take up work on his own initiative, retaining his position in the department and carrying on his work under the general supervision of the chief of his department.   There will always be a tendency in the departmental organization for men to desire to split away from the department to which they are attached and become semi-independent in the laboratory, and this tendency must be resisted in the organization and by the director of the laboratory.   At the same time, it is important that the control should not be so rigid that men feel that they are prevented from exercising their own initiative.

Twenty-five years later, the writer of this passage must acknowledge that it does not correspond to the realities of the situation.   Scientific research cannot really be organized under department leaders, who are themselves working scientists carrying out research work.   The fact is that the unit of scientific research is a *scientist* with a group of assistants and he is, by definition, capable of directing his own work by his own methods.   In the operation of his work, he must be independent of all control and free to do whatever he wishes. The function of his superior in the organization is not to control the operation of the work; it is to direct the work toward the problems that seem most desirable, to insure and assist co-operation between the individual research units, to provide the necessary working conditions and environment, and, in an industrial laboratory, to see that any results obtained are applied in practice.   This cannot be done by a man who is himself interested in his own scientific work since he will inevitably devote himself to research on certain problems, using some members of the department as assistants and leaving the rest of the department without control.   This statement can easily be challenged by those who have observed the successful direction of university laboratories by active scientific workers. Nevertheless, inquiry will show that even where the laboratory and its chief have become famous, the *direction* of the laboratory was weak, and success was due to the great skill shown by the chief and those who worked directly with him in his own problems. In a university laboratory, the junior scientists are there for only a short time; they are still learning the methods of research and will soon pass on to other positions. Neglect by a chief absorbed in his own problems can be tolerated by such men; but in an industrial laboratory or a research institute, where men spend their whole career, such neglect leads to much unhappiness and frustration.* The point at issue can be understood, perhaps from an analogy. The type of organization generally adopted is derived from the military analogy. The department leaders correspond to officers who give orders to their subordinates. But the true analogy of a scientific research organization is not an army; it is an orchestra. Each musician of an orchestra is important and independent; the members are correlated through the conductor, who is represented in the laboratory by the department head or in small laboratories by the director. It is not the duty of the laboratory head to command his scientific staff; it is his duty to lead it. Thus the military type of organization usually adopted for industrial labora-

---

* P. L. Kapitza (*Voks Bulletin*, No. 9–10 [1943]) believes that the director of a laboratory cannot be effective unless he works with his own hands. He says: "Only when one works in the laboratory oneself, with one's own hands, conducting experiments, even the most routine parts of them,—only under these conditions can real results be achieved in science. Good work cannot be done with other people's hands. A person who devotes ten or twenty minutes a day in directing scientific work can never be a great scientist. At least, I never saw or heard of a great scientist who worked in that manner, and I do not think it can be done. I am certain, that the very moment even the greatest scientist stops working in the laboratory himself, he not only ceases to develop but, in general, ceases to be a scientist." Kapitza, however, is speaking of an institute employing only a very few scientists, and he acknowledges that when the work expands and development work is involved, the time of the director will be taken up with other matters than work in the laboratory.

tories and even for research institutes, as shown in Figure 4, does not really operate at all. Instead, the operating system is that shown in Figure 5.

In a small laboratory, one having less than about twenty scientific men, no department heads for research work are necessary; the men can be responsible to the head of the

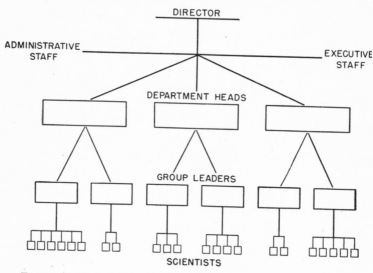

FIGURE 4. Formal Organization Chart of a Research Laboratory.

laboratory, who is generally known as the *director*. Any "service" or "development" divisions, on the other hand, should have efficient department heads in control of them so that the director can devote his attention to the scientific research without being distracted by the demands of those to whom the "service" is given. In a large laboratory, each section engaged in work in a special field should be responsible to a department head acting as an assistant director. Thus the organization of a large industrial laboratory might be represented by the chart shown in Figure 6.

The efficiency of a research laboratory depends to a very great extent upon the director. The qualifications of the director of a research organization are scientific ability, integrity of character, and energetic activity. There are scientists who are splendid research men and can operate with a small group of students or assistants and obtain most successful results, but who would be utterly useless in a large laboratory. They would not have the energy to keep in touch with the innumerable details of such a laboratory and, at the same

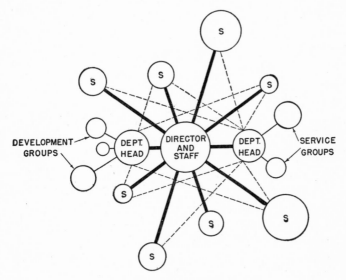

S — SCIENTIST AND ASSISTANTS

FIGURE 5. Approximation to the Actual Organization of a Laboratory of Medium Size.

time, to concentrate on the critical points in the research work and lead their men rapidly to a successful conclusion in each field of work in which such a conclusion became possible. Accounts of great research leaders always refer to them as spending time in the laboratory, discussing matters with their staff, helping or suggesting in one field after another, encouraging the despondent, and rejoicing with the successful.

The problems involved in finding suitable directors for industrial research laboratories are discussed later. In laboratories working in pure science, the difficulties are perhaps less, since it is not necessary to find a scientific man who is also capable in the commercial field. Nevertheless, the success of research institutes will depend to a large extent upon the choice of directors. The trustees of such institutes must find suitable directors for the institutes and then apply the

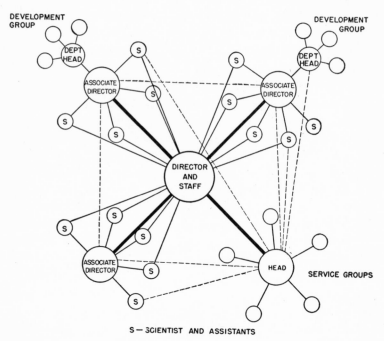

FIGURE 6. Approximation to the Actual Organization of a Large Laboratory.

pragmatic system to their enlargement or diminution. When an institute director is being successful and is producing valuable work, his field of activity should be enlarged and the institute given increased support. When he is doing only moderately well, it is probably unwise to expand his field even though he may blame insufficient support for his inability to produce results. Good men will produce results with a minimum of means, but as soon as they do so, the further means should be supplied.

Great care must be taken in the original selection of the director, since it is very difficult to remove him and his removal involves a great disruption of the work of the institute. Occasionally those responsible for the organization will realize that they have made a mistake—that the man they have chosen cannot do the work set before him—and then there should be no hesitation in making a change. This may seem an easy thing to do, but it is really very difficult. The great defect in management of all kinds is the tendency of those in authority to tolerate inefficiency rather than to face the unpleasant task of removing the inefficient. It is commonly believed that business men are harder in their dealings than public officials or executives in other walks of life. Anyone who has had much business experience will, however, agree, I think, that the greatest fault of business management is a tendency in personnel matters to avoid the issue because of weakness and sentiment. The motto for an executive of any kind in the treatment of those responsible to him is that he should be tough and he should be generous. He should demand a high standard of efficiency and endeavor to maintain it by making any changes that seem necessary, but he should be generous to the weaknesses of the inefficient and the misfortunes of the unlucky. It is unlikely, of course, that these principles for the selection and guidance of research directors will be carried out fully by any board of direction, but I believe that their application will be greatest if the controlling body consists primarily of scientific men.

The great danger is that the institutes might fall victims to a system of political jobbery and that the staff and even the director might be appointed for other reasons than their competence. This difficulty, however, would supply its own remedy. The institute would simply fail, and the advance of science, locally checked, would proceed elsewhere.

A problem that will arise if a considerable number of research institutes are supported by public funds will be the use and application of the results obtained. This will be complicated by the belief held by the public that a new technical development is largely accomplished when the original discovery is made, a belief which has been encouraged by scientists without industrial experience who believe that any delay in the application of a scientific discovery is due to malignancy on the part of industrialists rather than to the inherent problems of promoting a scientific discovery to the stage where it is of general use.

In industrial research we usually consider that the cost of the work in the research laboratory is of the order of 10 per cent of the total cost of developing an entirely new product to the point where it is ready for the market. Since the cost is an accurate measure of the energy involved, it is fair to consider that the original invention represents on the average only 10 per cent of the work involved in the development of a new product.

In a system of private enterprise, discoveries made in research institutes are not developed commercially unless those who develop them can see the possibility of a return for the work they have to do. If such discoveries are offered for development by the granting of non-exclusive patent licenses without any possibility of even a temporary monopoly being obtained, they will not be attractive to those who must spend much more money and energy than were required for the original discovery. On the other hand, the spirit of the time is quite opposed to the granting of an effective monopoly for even a moderate term of years. During the second World War, the Alien Property Custodian in the United States made available a large number of patents confiscated from enemy holders, but in the terms on which these patents are offered, there was a provision for an exchange of licenses if the licensee holds patents in the same field. This requirement of itself was sufficient to prevent industries from availing themselves of these patents to any great extent. The problems, therefore, arising from any attempt to control the use of discoveries and inventions of government-controlled research institutes are very great indeed. Probably by far the best solution would be to publish all the results, to take out no patents, and to leave the industrial world to apply whatever it could, obtaining its protection from the control of subsidiary inventions, which almost always arise in the development of a primary discovery.

The conclusions reached, therefore, as to the system of scientific research likely to develop in the future may be summarized as follows: The advancement of science will continue to depend upon the universities and upon the industrial laboratories, but much of the responsibility may be transferred to institutes devoted to special branches of science, probably supported by public funds and, it is to be hoped, controlled eventually by the scientific academies. If such a development comes to pass, it may be expected that science will advance more rapidly than at the present time; that society at large will recognize its dependence on the advance of science to a much greater extent than it does at the present time; and that there will be a considerable amount of insistence by both the general public and the official world on the planning and control of the scientific work.

There is at present much discussion of the value of planning for the promotion of scientific research, and the discussion has become somewhat embittered by its relation to party politics. The laissez-faire attitude of liberalism that pervaded intellectual thought in the nineteenth century is largely displaced today by the desire for a planned economy, which has developed from the writings of Marx, Engels, and their successors. This change arises from several causes, but mainly from the anxiety for the future that men feel today and from the rising importance in the intellectual life of the world of the engineers, to whom planning is a fundamental of life. If you have been educated chiefly by reading Plato and Euripides, you will have little faith in planning. If, on the other hand, you have been educated at an engineering school and have since spent your time in erecting buildings, making bridges, or designing automobiles, you will have much faith in planning. The people who dominated thought fifty years ago had been educated as classicists; the people who lead thought today have been educated as engineers. Which school of thought is right? The answer to this depends on what we want to do.

We can plan for the future and then we can carry out our plans provided that we remember the limitations of planning. We can only plan things that we can control, and our plans will be carried out only so long as our control is effective. We can plan production in a factory because we can control it. If the production is falling below our needs, we can increase it; if it exceeds them, we can diminish it. To plan, we need two things: first, the knowledge of the processes that we are attempting to control; second, the physical power to control those processes. It is when we extend our planning from the things that we know to the fields where our knowledge is weak and from the things that we can control to those that are in their nature uncontrollable that our planning fails.

When these principles are applied to the planning of scientific research, we find that the kinds of research that can be planned best are those which are least fundamental. Production can always be planned. The last stages of development can be planned with considerable certainty. When a new chemical has been made in the laboratory and the yields have been tested, a pilot plant must be built. The building of this pilot plant and even the time which it will take to test the processes on a moderate scale can be foreseen, and so in chemical factories pilot plant operation is usually carried out not as a research experiment but as a co-operative effort involving both the research men who originated the process and the production men who will operate it. Not infrequently the whole is under the direction of a chemical engineering group who specialize in pilot plant operations.

When more basic research is considered, planning necessarily becomes less certain. If we have made a new chemical in the laboratory, we know that we can make it in a pilot plant in spite of the fact that new problems may arise. But if the chemical has never been made or even if it has been made but the yields are unsatisfactory, we know less certainly how much time and effort will be required to get the process ready for a pilot plant test. Nevertheless, all applied research of this type can be planned and, to a considerable extent, should be planned.

When, however, we go back still further and attempt to discover an entirely new process, it is unlikely that any close planning of the work will be of value. In practice, what is done is to present the problem to a competent chemist and leave him to study parallel syntheses in the literature and to try one method after another which may lead to the result that he requires.

The chances of making discoveries that will advance a branch of science can be increased simply by having more men engaged in work in that field. Much of the recent advance in the science of astronomy has come from the accumulation of facts by a considerable number of observers, these facts being published and so made available for analysis by a limited number of skilled mathematical analysts. Many discoveries in astronomy have been made, as is said, "by accident," but the accident could only have occurred to an astronomer who was working in that field. The discovery of the sharp absorption lines produced by the scattered molecules of interstellar space, for instance, could not have been made unless astronomers had been photographing distant galaxies with powerful spectroscopes, and even then their detection depended upon the use of a comparatively fine-grained and therefore relatively insensitive photographic plate. Scientific discoveries of a basic type result, therefore, not from an attempt to make a given discovery but from concentration upon a special field of work by men using instruments of sufficient power and having sufficient skill to recognize the discoveries when they appear.

In the organization of scientific research, therefore, the value of planning varies from the necessity for detailed planning by engineering experts when a discovery is to be applied on a large scale to the most complete freedom of thought and experiment when we do not know what to look for and have no conception of what is likely to be found. As Dr. Baker said when discussing the discovery of the x-rays:

> If someone had thought it convenient to make the human body transparent, and had allocated money for the research, the result would have been a comprehensive plan, a team of research workers, a very large card index, a waste of money, and no x-rays. . . . Von Röntgen had no thought of trying to make human flesh transparent when he discovered the penetrating powers of x-rays. He was interested in the phenomena of electric discharge in high vacua, and did not guess that the result of his work would be the discovery that certain rays could be used in the diagnosis and treatment of human illness.[*]

A most interesting discussion on the planning of scientific research has arisen in the columns of the *New York Times* following the publication of the report by Bush to the President of the United States. The report was criticized in an editorial (*New York Times,* July 21, 1945) on the ground that it does not go far enough in providing for the planning of the work under the control of the federal government. This editorial brought a reply from J. B. Conant, who had through the war been the chairman of the National Defense Research Committee. Dr. Conant's views may be summarized by a quotation: "There is only one proved method of assisting the advancement of pure science—that of picking men of genius, backing them heavily, and leaving them to direct themselves. There is only one proved method of getting results in applied science—picking men of genius, backing them heavily, and keeping their aim on the target chosen."

In wartime, targets can be chosen with a reasonable degree of certainty and the second procedure succeeds. In pure science, no such objective can be defined. The subject was taken up by O. E. Buckley, president of the Bell Telephone Laboratories,[†] who protests against the idea that industrial

---

[*] John R. Baker, *The Scientific Life,* p. 59, London, George Allen and Unwin, Ltd., 1942.

[†] This is by far the largest research laboratory in the world, employing over five thousand people and costing about $30,000,000 a year.

research can be directed successfully from above. Buckley says: "One sure way to defeat the scientific spirit is to attempt to direct inquiry from above. All successful industrial research directors know this, and have learned by experience that one thing a 'director of Research' must never do is to direct research, nor can he permit direction of research by any supervisory board."

Buckley upholds Bush's plan, agreeing, however, that research efficiency can be improved by teamwork but objecting to the planning or "mapping out the field of science to reveal gaps in knowledge" suggested by the *New York Times*.

Warren Weaver, a prominent member of the directing staff of the National Defense Research Committee, believes that any attempt to use the methods effective during the war would be disastrous if employed to control scientific investigation during times of peace. He believes that national support for science should sponsor every movement and development that helps to create a favorable atmosphere for research but should by no means set up any group to chart its course.

In an article dated September 9, 1945, Waldemar Kaempffert, a scientific editor of the *New York Times,* insists that the advance of science should be accelerated by planning and organization, contrasting this with "the inefficient laissez-faire method of the past." He suggests that "a J. Willard Gibbs," who wanted to apply statistical mechanics to chemistry, might "join the organization" and "work happily in its atmosphere." Dr. Kaempffert says: "Whether such a man works alone or with others, no Director in his senses would tell him how he should proceed." When we remember the history of Willard Gibbs, it scarcely seems probable that if an organized research group had existed he would have been invited to join it or would have worked happily in its atmosphere.

W. R. Whitney, director of the great laboratory of the General Electric Company, the prototype of all industrial research laboratories, wrote in 1931:

> There exist two widely divergent paths by which mankind has advanced. One is Bacon's "variation in the ef-

ficient"—doing better in some ways what has already been done. It has become familiar to man in economics, in work of general welfare, in the mere mechanics of time-saving. The other path, extending beyond specific conceptions, leads to random and bold experiment—to pure research, where discovery is often unexpected. The most remarkable discoveries of the next eighty years will be of that kind.

It is interesting that even those who are most anxious to introduce the maximum of planning into the control of scientific research agree on its failure in regard to discoveries of the greatest importance. J. D. Bernal says:

In any survey of the business of scientific research, general lines of advance can be seen and fairly probable conclusions drawn from them. What cannot be seen are the possibilities of fundamental, new discoveries and their effect in revolutionizing the whole progress of science. The practical problem is to see that science advances on the widest and most comprehensive front, being prepared to accept and use as welcome gifts the radical discoveries that come in its way.*

This is in fact, of course, the abandonment of planning. It is these very revolutionary discoveries that make it impossible to plan the future of science.

When looking back, it is very easy to see how science could have been planned. Looking forward, all we can do is to continue to spread the frontiers of our knowledge and, as Bernal says, "to accept and use as welcome gifts the radical discoveries that come in our way."

Phillips † points out that since progress is made by trial and error, and its extent is therefore proportional to the number of trials, the conditions most favorable to progress will be those that favor the greatest number of trials. These conditions will be those where the number of *independent* thought centers is greatest, that is, the conditions of maxi-

* J. D. Bernal, *The Social Function of Science,* p. 343, New York, The Macmillan Co., 1939.

† Chapter II, page 19, footnote.

mum individual liberty. This is the true reason for the importance of personal liberty; progress depends on liberty. It is also the reason for the failure of any system for planning scientific research. The increase in efficiency of operation achieved by planning is balanced by the loss of independent thought, with a consequent diminution in the trial of ideas. This is especially true of the conduct of scientific research in the universities where any restriction of the liberty of investigators to choose their own work or even any inducement to follow lines chosen for them is to be deplored. It is even desirable that a large number of investigators should be forced, by lack of external suggestion, to find for themselves subjects for their work.

Chapter IX

APPLIED SCIENCE AND INDUSTRIAL RESEARCH

As we have seen, the application of science to industry developed first in the industries which themselves owed their existence to the growth of science, especially the chemical and electrical industries. The value of research in producing new materials and methods of manufacture slowly made it clear that in every industry in which technical processes were involved—and in what industries are they not involved?—organized scientific research was necessary if the industry was to survive and flourish. The thing that convinced business men of this was the age-old fear of competition. A man might believe that new scientific discoveries were of no value to him, but he could not entirely forget that his active competitor might take advantage of these discoveries—might, indeed, even be secretly making discoveries behind his back and might come out some day with a new line of products that would take his business away from him.

The primary function of the research department in an industry is to provide the scientific knowledge to meet difficulties, improve processes and products, and discover and develop new products; but in modern industry the research department has assumed broader functions. George Eastman once said that his research laboratory was "responsible for the future of photography." On the other hand, C. C. Paterson of the General Electric Company, Ltd., has said: "Industrial research exists in order that industry may have within itself those scientific resources in workers and equipment which will help the industry to cultivate the scientific outlook throughout all its personnel and activities." These two statements together may be taken as representing the ideals toward which every industrial research laboratory should strive.

In the early days of industrial research, a business assigned to it only a very small part of the executive budget. Confidence in the attainment of valuable results was small. If the use of science in the business succeeded, it was regarded as a kind of windfall. The success of the business depended, as in the past, upon the efficiency of production and selling. Businesses, at any rate all except the very largest, tend to be dominated by one of the great functional departments, such as that concerned with selling, in which case production is attuned to the needs of the sales department. In others, the more active and aggressive groups are those engaged in production, and these companies sell what they produce rather than produce what they need to sell. But with the growth of industrial research, the development and introduction of new products have become of such great importance that there are companies in which quite avowedly the research and development departments represent the primary driving force; the production departments manufacture the new products and the sales department sells them. In many companies the economic value of the research work is now fully recognized, and the financial journals devote a considerable amount of space to the development of industrial science.

The number and size of the industrial research laboratories have increased rapidly during the last thirty years. In the excellent monograph issued by the National Resources Planning Board, it is stated that since the first World War, industrial research in the United States has assumed the proportions of a major industry.* In 1920, about three hundred laboratories were engaged in industrial research. In 1940, the number had increased to more than 2200. The total personnel had grown from approximately 9000 to over

* *Report of the National Research Council to the National Resources Planning Board,* p. 37, U. S. Government Printing Office, Washington, D. C., 1941.

70,000. An estimate of the total expenditure on industrial research in the United States, based upon the cost per man in a number of laboratories, gives a total figure for 1940 exceeding $300,000,000. Since the increase in industrial research continued through the years of war, it is not unlikely that the total expenditure for 1945 was of the order of $500,000,000. Incidentally, these figures offer a complete refutation to the gloomy prophesies of certain "liberal" thinkers of thirty years ago. At that time, one of the arguments that Justice Brandeis used against the development of large units in industry was that they would infallibly neglect technical and scientific research and, thus, progress would be stifled by the operation of what he considered to be monopoly.*

Industrial research in the United Kingdom has grown rapidly both before and during the war. According to Dunsheath,† the direct expenditure of the Department of Scientific and Industrial Research was about $2,000,000 and of the Research Associations ‡ (in 1938) about as much again. Expenditure by private companies is much lower than in the United States but is still very considerable. A survey by the Federation of British Industries published in the early part of 1946 recorded 9000 graduate scientists engaged on research and development in British industry, with a total expenditure thereon of about £20,000,000 annually— a proposed increase of research staff of 25 per cent and of laboratory space of more than 2,000,000 square feet.

Industrial laboratories may be classified in three general divisions:

1. Plant laboratories exerting analytical and testing control over materials, processes, and product.

* The statement by Brandeis was actually quoted in 1944 by N. Kaldor at a conference on industrial research in England as if it represented a fact instead of a quite erroneous prediction!

† P. Dunsheath, "Industrial Research in Great Britain: a Policy for the Future," *Journal of the Royal Society of Arts,* **91,** 167, 242 (1943).

‡ Page 211.

2. Development laboratories working on improvements in product and processes, tending to lessen cost of production and to introduce new products on the market.

3. Laboratories working on pure theory and on the fundamental sciences associated with the industry.

Laboratories of the first type are so obviously necessary that practically all plants are equipped with them, and frequently each department of a factory maintains its own control laboratory.

Laboratories of the second class are frequently called "research" laboratories and have been largely instrumental in introducing scientific control into industry. In such a development laboratory, the work ranges from the simplest and most obvious alterations to problems of extreme difficulty involving scientific knowledge of a high order. The function of the development laboratory is to collect ideas from all sources and apply them to manufacture. Those investigations of the pure research section that result in new products or methods will usually pass through the development branch to the manufacturing departments. The man who has been in charge of an investigation in pure research should follow his work through the development branch into the manufacturing departments until it becomes a recognized and established feature in manufacture.

It is often desirable for the laboratory itself to have facilities for carrying new developments to the stage of production, and, indeed, in many laboratories it is considered necessary not only to manufacture on a small experimental scale but even to place certain new products on the market, transferring production to the works only when the demand is such that a full-scale manufacturing organization is required to meet it. This is particularly useful in the case of products that are new to the industry and that require novel and difficult manufacturing methods and, at the same time, the development of a new market.

If the whole future of an industry is dependent on the work of the research laboratory, then not merely an improvement in processes or a cheapening in the cost of manufacture will suffice, but fundamental work is required in the whole field in which the manufacturing firm is interested. For this purpose something very different from the usual plant laboratory is needed, and to maintain progress, the work of the research laboratory must be directed primarily toward the fundamental theory of the subject. This is a point that has sometimes been overlooked in discussions of industrial scientific research, much stress being generally laid upon the immediate returns to be obtained from plant laboratories and upon the advantage of scientific control of the operations. But in every case where the effect of research work in industry is very marked, that work has been directed not toward the superficial processes of industry, but toward the fundamental and underlying theory of the subject.

According to C. M. A. Stine of the Du Pont Company:

Fundamental research and what may be termed "pioneering applied research" should be differentiated. The distinction is based principally upon the scope of the work and the extent to which it is limited by certain recognized practical objectives. In general, research undertaken upon some broad general subject, such as the structure of cellulose, belongs to the category of fundamental research.

On the other hand, if a company engaged in the production of textiles coated with cellulose derivatives, or in the manufacture of photographic film, or of other products utilizing derivatives of cellulose, undertakes research aimed at the development of new cellulose derivatives, in the hope of developing such derivatives as might exhibit useful properties fitting them for application in manufactured products, the work becomes pioneering applied research. After the discovery of a new cellulose derivative and the evaluation of its properties, the next step might be actually to manufacture it, whereupon the investigation assumes the complexion of ordinary applied research.

The investigation of monomolecular films by a producer of electrical equipment might be fundamental research, whereas the investigation of monomolecular films by an oil refiner engaged in the production of lubricants might be largely in the field of applied research. Thus, the classification of the research depends upon the character of the problem and the nature of the agency carrying on the investigation.*

Fundamental research involves a laboratory very different from the usual plant laboratory. It requires a large, elaborately equipped, and heavily staffed laboratory engaged mainly in work that for many years is unremunerative and that, for a considerable time after its foundation, produces no results that can be applied to manufacture. Such a laboratory has a cumulative value as its work is continued. At the beginning it is of service to the industry in bringing a new point of view to bear on many of the problems; it is of value especially in establishing standard methods of testing and standard specifications for the purchase of raw materials, while much of its energy may profitably be devoted to the investigation of the use of the products of the industry. Many large industrial laboratories, indeed, are maintained as much in the interests of the customer as for the production departments. A research laboratory of this type also studies the merits of new industrial propositions of which the value has not been commercially established, but all these early uses of the laboratory eventually prove subsidiary to its main work on fundamental problems. When this main line of research begins to bear fruit, it absorbs the energies of both the laboratory and the factory. This, however, takes many years.

As explained previously, research laboratories may be of the divergent or convergent type. Those of the Bell Telephone Company, the General Electric Company at Schenectady, the Westinghouse Electric and Manufacturing Company, and the Eastman Kodak Company are essentially of the convergent type. The work of the research laboratory of

* Charles M. A. Stine, Vice President, E. I. du Pont de Nemours and Company, Wilmington, Del., "Fundamental Research in Industry, Research—A National Resource, II. Industrial Research." *Report of the National Research Council to the National Resources Planning Board,* p. 98, U. S. Government Printing Office, Washington, D. C., 1941.

the Eastman Kodak Company is concentrated primarily on the study of photography. The extent of its work in this field is shown by its publications. In the last thirty years, the laboratory has published about a thousand scientific papers, and of these by far the greater number deal with some aspect of the theory of photography. To take a single year: In 1936, papers were published on the formation of the latent image; the analysis of gelatin; the absorption spectra of cyanine dyes; the theory of image errors in lenses; the measurement of photographic densities; the stability of developers; the measurement of graininess; the decomposition of cellulose nitrate; the effect of sulfur compounds on photographic emulsions; and the application of quantum mechanics to the process of exposure.

In the divergent group of laboratories are included many research institutions that are interested in science in general or in science as applied to industry and that attack any problem promising progress in knowledge or, in the case of an industrial laboratory, financial return. The greater number of university and industrial laboratories are necessarily of this type. It would be a disadvantage for a university laboratory, whose primary business is training students, to be too narrowly specialized. Specialized university laboratories are desirable only for post-graduate students. Industrial laboratories, on the other hand, must be prepared to deal with any problems presented by the plant. As these are of all kinds, covering generally the whole field of physics, chemistry, and engineering, it is impossible for many plant laboratories to specialize except in so far as they deal with the plant processes themselves.

The position of an industrial research laboratory in the organization and its relation to the other departments of the company with which it is associated are of considerable importance.

Research laboratories have originated in many different ways. The earliest grew out of plant testing and control laboratories and were, therefore, responsible directly to the works manager. More recently, laboratories have generally been established as independent departments of the company and are responsible to the general manager only. If an executive of a manufacturing company is a technical scientific expert, he may have felt the need for a laboratory and established one under his own control. In this case, the laboratory is necessarily very closely associated with his work. A laboratory may have been established under a separate director, not himself associated with the executive officers of the company, as a reference department for the executives. In this case also the laboratory is closely associated with the officers of the company and tends to be concerned largely with questions of policy and the introduction of new products. In a large company, a research laboratory is usually established as a separate department, having its own organization and available as a reference department for all sections of the company.

The position that the research laboratory should occupy in an industrial organization is perhaps best determined by the criterion that the research department should be responsible to the officer of the company who is in charge of the development of new products. If the introduction of new products is in the hands of the plant organization, the research department should be responsible to the plant manager; if there is a definite development department, or, if new products are introduced through the agency of some definite executive, it is to that executive that the research department should be responsible. The research laboratory, in fact, should be associated primarily with development.

It cannot be too strongly emphasized that the success of the research laboratory depends upon the application of its work. Since application naturally depends to a great extent upon co-operation with other departments of the company, everything that promotes such co-operation is to be encouraged and anything different is to be discouraged. There is some question, on the other hand, whether the laboratory responsible for original work leading to new products should deal with manufacturing problems. If a research staff engaged on fundamental research is frequently called upon to deal with plant problems, the more fundamental work is subject to interruption and disrupted efficiency. At the same time, the study of plant problems suggests many important lines of work to the laboratory staff. Nothing is more stimulating to the co-operation of manufacturing departments with the laboratory than the successful solution by the laboratory of problems submitted by the plant departments. It is sometimes difficult for the laboratory to solve such problems. Very often the practical solution depends upon minute knowledge of the working process; and a laboratory is expected in some supernatural way to solve problems that have baffled men thoroughly acquainted with all aspects of the process. But even if the laboratory fails to solve a given problem to the satisfaction of the department concerned, the study of the process itself is quite likely to result in suggestions which may be of more value than the solution of the problem submitted. If the manufacturing organization is of sufficient size, a separate laboratory for the more fundamental problems may be desirable, leaving special departments of the laboratory better acquainted with manufacture to undertake those from the plant. Thus a link is formed between the purely scientific research and the manufacturing departments.*

While a large laboratory fully equipped for fundamental research represents the most effective means of prosecuting industrial research, such a laboratory can be maintained only by large manufacturing companies, as the cost of maintenance is very heavy and only a large company can afford such an expenditure. On the other hand, national industry is not carried on principally by large manufacturing companies, either in the United States or in Great Britain. In Britain, 98 per cent of the factories are said to employ less than a thousand workers, and 80 per cent less than a hundred. Probably the situation is the same in the United States. The chief

* P. G. Nutting, "Research and the Industries," *Scientific Monthly*, **7**, 149 (1918).

problem, therefore, in the application of science to national industry is presented by the smaller businesses that cannot afford to maintain a really large laboratory. In Great Britain, the solution offered by those responsible is membership in one of the research associations organized under the Department of Scientific and Industrial Research to serve entire industries.

A conference on problems of scientific and industrial research was held in 1944 at Nuffield College, Oxford, England, and an excellent summary of the discussion was published by the Oxford University Press.* In this report the operations of the research associations are described. The British Research Associations were formed during the first World War when the British government at the end of 1916 announced its intention to allot £1,000,000 for the formation and maintenance by the Department of Scientific and Industrial Research of approved associations for research in co-operation with the industries. The plan was to form associations of which approximately half the cost would be paid by the industries and the remainder by the government, these associations to carry out systematic research and to apply science to the problems of industry. The scheme was widely approved, and by the end of 1920, thirteen research associations had been formed. The total number to date is just under thirty.

In the twenty odd years since the first associations were formed, the plan has met with little opposition, yet those men who have been most closely connected with the research associations have, on the whole, been disappointed, a disappointment which is commonly attributed to the lack of funds. The sum of £1,000,000 was, of course, utterly inadequate for research relating to the whole of the British industry; yet it was found difficult to raise an equal sum from the industries. Undoubtedly, funds could be raised after a research associa-

* *Problems of Scientific and Industrial Research,* Oxford University Press, April 1944.

tion had demonstrated its value; on the other hand, it is very difficult for a research association to do this until it has the funds. After the first ten years' work of the department, the advisory council in their review in 1925–1926 said that, when they reflected how trivial in relation to the total output of an industry is the expenditure needed, they could not believe that private enterprise would fail to maintain on an adequate basis the associations that had already shown their value. Nevertheless, the council believed that voluntary contributions would be inadequate and favored the introduction of some kind of compulsory levy. After this report had been issued, there was a gradual improvement in the financial support of the associations, and under war conditions it has increased, although it is still inadequate.

The Nuffield report goes on to discuss the objectives of the research associations. Should they, for instance, undertake long-term programs of applied research, study the scientific facts on which the processes of the industries are based, and merely publish their results, leaving it to the firms to apply them to their own work? Or should the research association translate as much as possible of its work into results that can be applied by the industry even though the individual firms have no adequate scientific staffs? Again, should the associations devise their own research programs or should they be ready to study problems proposed by any subscribing firm and advise such firms how to deal with their own specific problems? The conference felt that there could be no uniform answer to these questions. The answer would depend upon the industry. Modern scientific industries such as the electric or scientific instrument industries need a different policy from that of the older technologies, such as the textile or leather industries. In the more technical industries, the individual firms have their own laboratories, and they allot to the research association only long-term problems suitable for collective effort. In the older industries, where the processes are still largely based on tradition, the research associations have a double function. On the one hand, they must study short-range problems, which offer immediate results; on the other, they should certainly undertake a long-range study of the fundamental scientific problems of the industry that have been neglected in the past. Thus the older industries need an active program of scientific research much more than the modern industries, but it is much more difficult to do this work and to obtain support for it. Some industries, such as those dealing with textiles, are divided between the successive stages of production. The research association must think in terms of the industry as a whole rather than of a single section. In the cotton industry, for instance, there are not only the problems of the spinning, weaving, dyeing, bleaching, and finishing branches, but there are also the problems of the cotton plant itself and of the raw material that it produces.

Most research associations are faced with the problem of combining a variety of functions in one institution. If the association concentrates on the major long-run problems, many of the smaller firms with immediate difficulties will be dissatisfied. If, instead, it deals primarily with service work, it may degenerate into a mere testing station, and will certainly lose the good will of larger firms to whom it is giving little information of value.

Research associations cannot take the place of the research laboratories of the industry itself. In the latter, the new developments achieved are important for the individual firm. They give that firm advantage over its competitors and an improved position in the industry, and they bring to the laboratory, therefore, the enthusiastic support of the other parts of the organization. No company capable of doing its own research will pass to an association serving its competitors equally with itself the problems that seem to it most promising.

While the British Research Associations have undoubtedly been useful to the small units in their industries, they cannot be considered on the whole to have promoted the establishment of research laboratories in the individual companies of the industry. The examples of successful research have, of course, tended in this direction and, in many cases, may have induced manufacturers to form their own research groups. But their effect in this direction has been offset to some extent by the tendency on the part of the financial heads of the industries to assume that membership in a research association is sufficient to take care of their scientific needs.

In the United States there are a few organizations comparable to the British Research Associations. Most firms, however, have their own centralized research laboratories or utilize the facilities of large endowed laboratories such as the Mellon Institute, Battelle Memorial Institute, or the Armour Research Foundation, which may conveniently be called Technological Research Institutes.

The Mellon Institute, at the University of Pittsburgh, the prototype of these laboratories, was founded in 1911 to carry out the scheme of industrial fellowships originally introduced by Robert Kennedy Duncan of the University of Kansas. Duncan adopted this scheme partly to train students in industrial research and partly because he felt that such research work as was attempted in small factories was often undertaken under very bad conditions.* He felt too that the manufacturer often has neither the knowledge nor the experience requisite to establish successful research, that he is not willing to allow sufficient space or equipment for it, and that a man working alone in a small industry is hampered both by lack of the stimulation he might get from association with other scientific workers and by want of proper skilled direction of the work.

In such a laboratory as the Mellon Institute, the manufacturer can arrange to have the work done under conditions that insure that he alone obtains the result of the work; and yet the research men will have the advantages of the Institute, contact with other scientific workers, the availability of

---

* R. K. Duncan, "Industrial Fellowships," *Journal of the Society of Chemical Industry,* **28,** 684 (1909).

sources of information such as a reference library, and direction of the work by experienced administrative officers of the laboratory. According to the system in operation at the Mellon Institute, a manufacturer having a problem that requires solution may become the donor of a fellowship, which provides the salary of the fellow selected, and the Institute supplies laboratory space and the use of all ordinary chemicals and equipment.

In 1944–1945, there were 94 industrial research programs in operation, employing 242 scientists and 232 assistants. The service staff of the Institute numbered 169, and total expenditure was slightly more than $2,000,000. The subjects under investigation were diversified: for instance, catalysis as related to the synthesis of butadiene; utilization of corn products, such as starch, oil, and zein; improvement in waste disposal in streams; structural glass; coal and coke products; synthetic lubricants; properties of cotton fibers; petroleum products; organic silicon resins; industrial hygiene.

The Battelle Memorial Institute was founded by Gordon Battelle, industrialist, whose will provided for the building and endowment of an independent institute "for the purpose of education . . . the encouragement of creative research . . . and the making of discoveries and inventions" for industry. Its operation began in 1929.

In its plan, Battelle provides the plant, equipment, and staff. The company or group under whose auspices the research is done pays for the time of the personnel assigned to the project and the out-of-pocket costs. Sponsored research at Battelle in 1945 was estimated at $3,000,000, and the laboratories housed a staff of approximately 800 technologists and assistants. Each project undertaken is the responsibility of the Institute as a whole, and, using the methods of group research, all equipment and the knowledge of the entire staff of technologists in diversified fields can be brought to bear on the solution to a technological problem. In addition to its research work, Battelle conducts a program that offers training to selected young men who plan to follow industrial research as a career.

The Armour Research Foundation developed in 1936 from industrial research directed by the faculty of the Armour Institute of Technology. It has grown very rapidly and in the year 1943–1944 had in operation 117 long-term projects with a total budget of $1,670,000. It carries on its work under a plan whereby each problem is subjected to the collective thinking and co-operative action of a permanent staff of research workers in many fields of science, and in which every possible routine operation is removed from the research worker's responsibility and placed in the hands of auxiliary service laboratories.

In general, these technological research institutes are increasing both in size and in number and are rendering a great service to American industry. During the year 1945 alone, two new ones were founded—the Southern Research Institute, at Birmingham, Alabama, and the Midwest Research Institute, at Kansas City, Missouri. Research facilities are thus made conveniently available to industries within these regions. The institutes provide equipment, often on a semi-plant scale, that would not otherwise be available for experimental work, and they often specialize in certain fields of work with a long-range, continuous program approximating to the work of a specialized research group. They are also of great value for training men; and in many cases manufacturers who have endowed an industrial fellowship eventually establish research laboratories of their own, employing in them the men who have carried on the work as fellows. These technological institutes thus serve as nurseries for private industrial research laboratories in addition to doing work directly and training men. This influence is of the greatest importance, because however effective is the actual research work done in an external laboratory, that work should supplement rather than take the place of scientific work done as an integral part of the business.

The technological status of industry has little permanency. It is often assumed that those firms that have developed large amounts of technical skill will continue to dominate their industries and that other industries will remain without any corresponding scientific guidance. This is not true, however, as the Nuffield College report points out. Industrial progress depends not only on the existence of large firms carrying on research over a wide field but equally on the continual emergence of new firms animated by a scientific spirit in their approach to industrial problems.

Before 1920 the petroleum industry of the United States, one of the most wealthy and powerful industries, did very little scientific research. Since then it has not merely established scientific divisions and research laboratories, but it has come to the very forefront of industrial scientific research and has developed entirely new branches of industrial chemistry. This is no rare phenomenon. Again and again, a change in management or the emergence in management of one individual has revolutionized a manufacturing company and eventually an industry. Thus, instead of a picture of a static industrial world in which there are giants and pygmies, the facts show a world in which the giants must work unceasingly to remain strong and the pygmies are continually growing and asserting their right to a place in the sun.

It is asserted far too often that "small businesses cannot afford to support scientific research." Few businesses *can* afford to *support* research. They carry out their research, as they do the rest of their operations, for profit, that is, to be supported by it; and if they are successful, they do not remain small, they grow. When Ernst Abbe joined Carl Zeiss, he entered a very small business, which became the leading optical industry of the world. When Ludwig Mond joined John Brunner, he founded a business which became one of the chief components of Imperial Chemical Industries.

The Zeiss firm or the alkali works of the future are today small firms *with an active leader* imbued with the spirit of science. The problem for the small business, in fact, is not how to get its scientific work done by somebody else but *how to find that active leader.*

When the first industrial research laboratories were organized, in the early years of this century, the managers of industrial undertakings realized that they required a group of investigators whose results could be applied to that particular industry. They realized also that they themselves did not understand how scientific work was carried out or how it could be applied. They therefore chose an individual, frequently a teacher of science at a university, who was employed to enter the industrial organization as director of research. Characteristically, the first task assigned to the research director was usually to build a laboratory, an operation which he undertook with the enthusiasm and zest born of ignorance, since very few scientific men know anything about buildings. Having built the laboratory, the research director proceeded to organize a staff and to start doing scientific research. The success of these early pioneers varied considerably, but almost all were successful to some extent.

The efficiency and accomplishment of an industrial laboratory depend to a very large extent upon the director. In fact, it may be said of research laboratories, as of other human institutions, that they are the reflex of a man. The large industrial research laboratories are at the present time passing through a critical stage, in which the founding directors are passing and are being replaced by their successors. Their experience shows to how great an extent the success of a research laboratory is dependent upon the individuality of its director. There are laboratories which have had a distinctly successful career and which, with the passing of the directors who organized and developed them, have fallen into obscurity. Moreover, it is extremely difficult to find suitable men to direct industrial laboratories. Such a man must be both a scientist and an executive, and he must have an interest in and a capacity for the commercial operations of the business in which he is engaged. The reason that the director of an industrial research laboratory must be interested in the commercial operations of his company is that he *must* make his laboratory pay; and if he does not know how to do that, no one else can do it for him.

It is even more difficult to select a director for the research department of a small company than for the large laboratory of a great manufacturing concern. The ideal would be a man who combined the necessary scientific ability and experience with definite capacity for the executive operation of a business, so that he could very soon become one of the senior officers in charge of the business.

Unfortunately, though the necessary characteristics are not really rare, there is no source to which those responsible for the conduct of business can turn for guidance in their selection. What is needed is a staff college or university department where scientists who wish to specialize in the application of science can obtain post-graduate training of the type supplied by the Harvard School of Business Administration and where they will be known to be available for positions. The establishment of such colleges or departments in Great Britain and the United States would go far toward supplying the present need for the increased application of science in the smaller businesses.

C. G. Renold * in his address to the Manchester Chamber of Commerce realized that the application of science to a small business required the services of a scientist with executive functions. Since he assumed, however, that such a concern could not set up its own research department and would rely on a co-operative laboratory, he suggested the appointment of a "Scientific Liaison Officer" to formulate problems and interpret the answers into practice. If such an officer were competent, he would almost certainly want to do research work under his own direction and would establish a laboratory. Perhaps, however, there are business managements to whom the idea of a "liaison officer" might seem less startling and dangerous than a research director.

* *Science and Industry,* p. 28, Manchester Chamber of Commerce, King St., Manchester 2, England, 1944.

The actual direction of industrial research is a matter of great importance and one on which there is much difference of opinion. The fundamental problems are what researches are to be done, along what lines is work to be started, how long is it to be kept going when the prospects for success look bad, when is loss to be cut and the work abandoned? These problems are at the heart of the whole matter, and the decisions with regard to them constitute the direction of research.

As business managements have become familiar with the use of science and its importance to industry has increased, managements have tended to become more and more interested in the actual direction of the scientific work. They no longer feel that the research director can be left to initiate work along the lines that he thinks are likely to be profitable, to exploit his idiosyncrasies, or even to play his "hunches." They consider it necessary to operate the research and development sections because the future of the business depends upon it. The research director must expect to receive direction and instructions from the management of the company, and must expect to have to justify the plans that he puts forward. This tendency is common among almost all the companies in which industrial research has been successful.

As a result of the anxiety of management to supervise the work of the research department, there has arisen a system of control that is sometimes known as the *project system*. According to this, the research manager proposes a plan of research divided into a large number of individual projects, to each of which are allocated certain definite funds. This plan is considered by various groups and, finally, by a special committee of the executives of the company assigned to the task, and is approved both in whole and in detail. The work done is reported periodically, and the expenditure on each project is considered in relation to the original allocation of funds for that purpose, new funds being allocated as necessary, and each project being finally closed either as a success or as a failure that must be abandoned. This project system may be regarded as one extreme in the control of the research work.

The other extreme, almost universal in the early days of industrial research, is the direction of the research by an individual responsible only to the top management of the company and without supervision in his own work. To him, the company entrusts the funds that it proposes to spend, and from him the company asks only results, with such accounting controls as insure merely that the funds have been expended for research in accordance with ordinary business principles. This method regards the whole of the research expenditure frankly as a gamble in which the management, having hired an expert in the field, leaves it to him and to his men to spend their funds in the hope that the company will get an adequate return. The project system regards research as a business which can be organized, and, while recognizing that some of the projects will fail, proposes that the successful ones should carry the failures. Viewed in this way, the project system will be far more attractive to business management than the opposite system, in which control over the choice of research projects is exercised only by the research men.

In assessing the relative advantages of the project system and of the individual direction of industrial research, we must consider their relative efficiency and their cost. The overhead cost of a laboratory operated on the project system is necessarily greater than that of a laboratory operated without it, so that it should be demonstrably more efficient if it is to be worth while.

The development of new products for the market, like production itself, can be organized and planned; so can the service work. But when we turn to the scientific work of the laboratory, to the researches from which new discoveries may come, any systematized planning becomes difficult and perhaps impossible. This can be met by the direct allocation of certain funds for this fundamental work. It enables the scientific men to carry out work that no committee would approve or could direct and, to a great extent, meets the most serious objection to the operation of the project system.

For the direction of the service and the development problems, which in most laboratories represent the greater portion of the work, the project system would be preferable were it not for the fact that it costs a great deal more. The project system requires a complete accounting system, a great deal of reporting involving stenographic assistance and filing, and, in addition, it consumes an immense amount of time, both of the scientific staff and of the management of the company, spent on the careful consideration of the various projects. In many large laboratories, much of the time of the senior scientific staff is devoted to conferences and committee meetings at which the problems of the laboratory are discussed in detail. This is so serious that some laboratories openly state that it is undesirable for the best scientific men to be group leaders since they are left little time for scientific work and that the scientific experts should have their work directed by a group leader who is essentially a business man with scientific training. It is very difficult to calculate accurately the relative costs of the two systems, but with certain simplifying assumptions, it is not impossible to make guesses.

    1. Let us assume that in both systems the scientific men are paid the same amount.

    2. Let us assume that in both systems the scientific men are of the same average ability.

Then the cost by the two systems per scientific man employed for the same total amount of work done can be measured by the total cost of the laboratories. According to available figures, the cost of some laboratories run by the project system is approximately $10,000 a year for each scientific man working in the laboratories; in laboratories without the project system, in which the work is directed only by the scientific staff, the average cost is of the order of $7000 per man per year.*

  * These figures date from 1930; they have undoubtedly increased, but the proportion will be unaffected.

Thus, under the project system, the work of a scientific man costs approximately 40 per cent more than if there were no external control of the work done. In addition, it must be remembered that no allowance is made for the time of the company executives not in the laboratory who assist in the supervision of the laboratory work.

For the project system to be worth while, therefore, from a purely commercial point of view, it must be assumed that approximately 40 per cent of the work of the scientific men in a laboratory operating without the system will be misdirected and could be eliminated by the use of the project system. It is doubtful that this is the case, and it is probable that the project system materially increases the cost of operating a research laboratory and does not produce an equivalent efficiency in results.

In the unplanned laboratories, many mistakes are made. These are evils of commission. Probably the project system avoids them to some extent, but under the project system there are more likely to be errors of omission. The errors of commission are visible to the management; the errors of omission are invisible because unknown. If a piece of work that costs $100,000 ends in failure, it is obvious, and it appears reasonable to everybody that the man responsible should be brought to account for it and told not to make the same mistake another time. There is no real danger of his doing so, of course; next time he will make a different mistake. On the other hand, an error of omission, in which the possibility of a most valuable development is not recognized, is unknown even to the director himself, since he will be satisfied, in the characteristic human fashion, that his judgment was probably right. There is only one case where an error of omission can be evaluated. It is where it has been decided to make a change in the plans—not to do a thing or to stop doing something; then, for no reason directly connected with the decision, it is not put into effect and the work is carried on. For instance, a suggestion for a particular piece of research is considered by the scientific men concerned and by the director in the light of the information he has. They decide not to do it, but then the legal department reminds them: "You have forgotten that we made a contract in which we agreed to carry out this piece of work." The success or failure of the work, then, is a clear test of the validity of the original decision. In three cases from the author's experience, where the decision had been made to abandon a piece of work but where it was carried forward without any change in opinion and for quite other reasons, the work proved entirely successful. Experiences of this kind demonstrate how difficult it is to make plans for the conduct of research and even the decisions essential for its operation.

The experience of the last thirty years suggests that the greatest success has attended those industrial research laboratories in which the director has been permitted a high degree of autonomy and an assurance of continued support. Industrial research is an adventure; it is even a gamble, though one in which the odds are on success, provided that the work is continued in spite of delays and discouragements. Such an adventure demands from its sponsor much courage and much confidence. But if the director and his staff are well chosen, the confidence will not be misplaced, and the rewards will be commensurate with the risks.

Chapter X

THE PATH OF SCIENCE

In the early chapters of this book, we followed the growth of human civilization. We saw in the history of that growth the mounting knowledge of science, visible first as the rationalization of technology and then pursued for its own sake. It was found convenient to represent the history of civilization as a helix, in which the cyclic structure discernible in the arts is shown in the coils, and the cumulative growth of knowledge is shown as the vertical component. It will be recalled that at the beginning the vertical component was small and the coils, representing the cycles of civilization, lay closely upon one another. With the coming of the Graeco-Roman culture, organized knowledge developed, and in the seventeenth century, after the invention of printing and the discovery of the experimental method, modern science came into existence. At the present time, the progress of science is so rapid that it dominates the whole world picture and challenges the ability of the leaders of mankind to meet the social changes that it produces.

As we follow the path of science through the ages, we can note certain points at which the scientific method was applied to a new group of the problems that confronted mankind. These are not the points at which the major discoveries and inventions were made; they are the occasions when new applications of the scientific method emerged. Perhaps the first of these occasions may be chosen as that at which causation was realized—when it was understood that like causes beget like effects and, as a result, rational technology was born. Another turning point in history came after the invention of writing, when the methods and formulae for technology were written down and so preserved and transmitted, a point that in Egyptian history is associated with the work of the architects and engineers who carried out the great buildings of the Old Kingdom, including the Pyramids. In the later Greek period, from 400 B.C. to 200 B.C., the relation of science to philosophy emerged; logic and mathematics evolved as the tools of thought; and the epistemology of science developed. In the seventeenth century, the experimental method was discovered; and the development of the body of valid ideas, which today we term *science,* proceeded apace.

At the beginning of the twentieth century, the experimental method of science was found to be directly applicable to the control of industry, and from that application has come the rapid growth in the efficiency of production that has marked the present age.

But the path of science is not ended. As Joan Evans says: "The present should retain its true proportion . . . a moment between an infinite past and a hurrying future." In that future, there are already signs of a new field for the application of the methods of science, the field of the social sciences—sociology, economics, and politics.

The application of the methods of science to the social sciences is by no means novel. Plato and Aristotle discussed it and, indeed, regarded the understanding of the principles of political economy as the chief end of scientific investigation. Francis Bacon laid down the application of science to politics as the principal object of the pursuit of knowledge. The philosophers of the eighteenth and nineteenth centuries based much of their sociological and economic doctrines upon the supposed nature of scientific knowledge. Two of those philosophers, holding very different political views, Herbert Spencer and Karl Marx, founded all their sociological precepts upon what they believed to be the teachings of science.

A. N. Whitehead, however, points out that the whole tradition of the thinkers who have written on sociology and political philosophy is warped by the assumption that each generation follows the practices of its fathers and transmits to its children the conditions that it finds in society.* For the first time in history, this assumption is false (compare Chapter I, page 10 ff.). Moreover, since the social and economic changes characteristic of the present age are produced by the development of science, they increase as the development of science accelerates. As Whitehead says: "Today we are at the beginning of a new crisis of civilization, which gives promise of producing more fundamental change than any preceding advance. . . . The whole of human practical activity is in process of immediate transformation by novelties of organized knowledge." † This is true because the growth of science is not only very rapid, but *it is still accelerating.* The production of new science, in fact, is accelerated by the science already produced; and this phenomenon is parallel to that which the chemist knows as an *autocatalytic reaction.*

Autocatalytic reactions are those in which the product of the reaction itself increases the rate at which the reaction proceeds. If we heat guncotton, that most important explosive, it gives off a little nitric acid, which makes it decompose faster, so that it gives off more nitric acid and decomposes faster and faster until finally the heat generated may be sufficient to produce an explosion. Any chemical reaction that produces heat will increase autocatalytically if the heat is not conducted away. Such a reaction is interesting to watch. We put the solvent in a vessel, add all the ingredients, and perhaps warm them a little. Then, the reaction starts and generates heat as it proceeds. It goes faster and faster, and the solution may rise in the vessel and froth; and then, as the reaction decreases and the materials are used up, the solution sinks again. If there is not enough room, the vessel will boil over; if there is enough room, it will undergo a complete transformation into a new system. The termination of the reaction is produced by the exhaustion of one of the com-

* A. N. Whitehead, *Adventures of Ideas,* p. 117, New York, The Macmillan Co., 1933.

† "Statesmanship and Specialized Learning," *Proceedings of the American Academy of Arts and Sciences,* 75, No. 1, p. 5 (1942).

ponents, just as the production of plankton in the sea is limited by the supply of mineral salts, principally phosphate, in the water. In northern latitudes, the phosphate in the surface water is renewed by the change of temperature in the spring and in the fall. As the temperature of the surface water in the spring rises to 28° centigrade, it becomes heavier than the colder water and sinks, bringing to the surface a supply of fresh water containing phosphate. This is followed by an outburst of plankton growth limited only by the minerals available.

If the autocatalytic production of science is limited by some factor necessary to it, it will accelerate until that factor becomes exhausted and then settle down to progress at a rate dependent upon the supply of the factor. Up to the present, no such limiting factor for the production of scientific knowledge is apparent.

As the production of new knowledge and of new inventions goes on, the conditions under which we live change, and we have to adjust our lives to meet the changing conditions. Sometimes adjustment is delayed either because the need for it is not realized or because some group having power in the society resists any adjustment. Then, when the adjustment comes, it is violent. Our efforts should be directed, therefore, so that we can adjust our social conditions continuously as the advance of science makes changes necessary, and so that we recognize that the world today is a changing world and not the relatively static world of the past.

The realization of the need for adjustment has led many thinkers to the conclusion that the method of adjustment is simple, that all that is required is to plan changes in our social and economic systems to meet the advances of science. It is believed that by planning we can avoid the difficulties and disasters that afflict us in the absence of a central planning organization. This goes so far in some circles that it is even proposed to plan scientific discovery, but it is equally impossible to plan in detail the economic future of a society. The reason is the same. We do not know what discoveries are possible; we do not know what will happen to our economics in the near future; nobody knows.

It is not even possible to plan the whole conduct of a war, at least if the war is to be won. There is little doubt that the German and the Japanese staffs had complete plans for the war that they have just lost. Those who defeated them, of course, planned their operations, their supplies, and their production. But these plans were based on fundamental principles and were subject to instant change as the conditions of the struggle changed. For this reason, prophesies as to the course of the war had no validity; and an excellent lesson in the weakness of human prevision can be obtained by reading any book written between 1930 and 1945 that deals with the probable course of the struggle between Germany or Japan and their opponents. In politics and economics, the lesson is the same: No one foresaw the Great Depression, the long-continued New Deal administration in the United States, or even such an isolated event as the fall from power of Winston Churchill at the end of the European War.[*]

The progressive adjustment of social organization to meet the rapid changes produced by the development of science and technology cannot be determined by the direct transfer of the techniques used in the physical and natural sciences. As von Hayek points out, there are great differences between the methods of the physical sciences and those of the social sciences.[†] The scientist confronted with the problems of sociology tends to imagine a theoretical society that will follow the principles of physical science and which he can therefore understand. This is clearly marked in the social philosophy of Comte and Saint-Simon and in the suggestions of the "technocrats" and of J. D. Bernal and J. G. Crowther with their idea of "frustration" (Chapter III, page 62).

[*] H. B. Phillips, "On the Nature of Progress," *American Scientist,* 253 (1945).

[†] F. A. von Hayek, "Scientism and the Study of Society," *Economica,* N.S., **10**, 39 (1943).

This application of the methods of physical science to the study of society has been extended to history, so that those who believed that a cyclic pattern could be discerned in history have desired or have been urged to "verify" their theory by relating it to the present course of events or even by prophesying the future. If the prophecies were confirmed, the theory would be "verified," just as the reappearance of Halley's comet confirmed the calculations of that great astronomer. This is, of course, absurd; we know nothing of the future, and the actors in the drama of history cannot possibly understand the part that they themselves play in that drama. This is true in fact, and it is also true even if we assume that, when viewed from the standpoint of the future, the present happenings will fall into a definite pattern. If we are prepared to accept provisionally Petrie's cyclic theory (which can only be justified strictly for art), a glance at Figure 1 (Chapter II, page 32) will show that according to Petrie the present corresponds to the end of the medieval cycle, while the modification suggested in Figure 2 places the present at the rising stage of a modern cycle. Which is right cannot be determined for several hundred years even if the cycles continue unperturbed by the unprecedented rise of science.

While the techniques of the physical sciences cannot be transferred to the field of sociology, the scientific method itself can and must be used for the study of the structure of society, its reaction to changing conditions, and the adjustments required to enable it to retain stability as those conditions change. An example of the application of the scientific method to a primitive society is Malinowski's * study of the social organization of the Trobriand islanders, which depends upon the elaborate ceremonial trading system known as the *kula*. A scientific study of modern industrial society by T. N. Whitehead † is based to some extent upon field

* B. Malinowski, *Argonauts of the Western Pacific*, London, Routledge, 1922.

† T. N. Whitehead, *Leadership in a Free Society*, Cambridge, Harvard University Press, 1936.

studies made by the Western Electric Company in their factories. Whitehead points out that any group in society en-
deavors to insure its own survival, and that if changes are to
be acceptable they must originate within the group, prefer-
ably as from the established leader of the group. Thus the
conservative forces of society can be overcome by evolution
from within but they will oppose changes from without. The
trade union movements or the co-operative movements are
based upon the support of the individual members, many of
whom have been active in their development. In the same
way, a new religion makes rapid headway as a spontaneous
movement among the people, only to be resisted to the death
when its followers attempt to impose it upon others. Modern
society, however, has an economy based upon machine industry, and this industry is engaged in continual never-ending
change controlled by relatively logical, scientific thinking.
The result has been an increasing clash between the conservative instincts of the various groups of society and the
interests of the industrial leaders whose operations imperil
the continuance of those social groups.

As Whitehead says, it is impossible to resist the changes produced by the impact of technology even if such a resistance
were desirable. "So the next stage in the progress of an industrial society is surely to increase the range of systematic
thinking to include not only the technological processes but
also the social processes which hold men together." *

Twenty-five years ago, scientists were believed by the lay
public to be impractical, absent-minded people devoid of
administrative ability or common sense. Today public opinion has swung to the opposite extreme, and it is even urged
that men trained in the methods of scientific research should
enter political life and endeavor to obtain a controlling position in the administration of the commonwealth. As Bernal
says, "This solution suffers from two radical objections: first,
that no one can think of any way of transferring control into

* T. N. Whitehead, *loc. cit.*, p. 84.

their hands; and, second, that most existing scientists are manifestly totally unfitted to exercise such control." *

There are, indeed, certain characteristics of scientific thinking that make it difficult for scientists to operate in the political sphere. The age-old foe of the scientific method is authority, and for a scientist to accept authority is to abandon his faith. But an almost equally objectionable idea to the scientific mind is that a decision should be made under the influence of emotion, and in politics emotion plays a very great part. In most political matters we do not think; we feel. One who claimed to know him praised a certain national statesman, whereupon his listener reminded him that though the statesman might be the wisest and noblest of mankind, he was yet a man and not a god. When, a few years later, the eulogist had changed his political views, he was reminded that the statesman might be the vilest and basest of mankind, but he was a man and not a devil.

The cleavage in intellectual outlook and mental habits between the political leader and the scientist, the engineer, or, for that matter, the industrialist is a very real and fundamental one and is by no means to be dismissed summarily. It is common for scientists and industrialists to discuss the methods of the politician as if he were either merely stupid or deliberately wicked,† while the views of the political expert on the "intellectuals" are often scornful in the extreme.

As long as men's actions are controlled by their emotions, an objective thinker who discusses every proposition without emotion can have no part in modern political life, since a politician must understand the effect of emotional thought and must be prepared to utilize emotional appeal if he is to

* Bernal, *The Social Function of Science*, p. 398.

† An antidote for this error can be found in F. W. Oliver's *The Endless Adventure* (London, Macmillan and Co., 1930). The section "Some Modern Dilemmas" should be of particular value to those prone to facile criticism, while that "In Praise of Politicians" presents an excellent picture of the debt we owe to those who govern us. See also "The Magnitude of the Task of the Politician," F. M. Davenport, *Harvard Business Review*, **III**, 468 (1933).

obtain popular support. A successful political leader must tend, therefore, either to believe his own emotional appeal or to become a cynic and to some extent a hypocrite if he exerts that appeal without belief. It is this difficulty that makes even the greatest democratic leaders seem insincere in many of their actions. The appeal to emotion is unavoidable if popular sanction is to be obtained, and yet their critics and often they themselves in retrospect feel that appeal to be false and unwarranted. For this reason alone the political arena would seem to be unsuitable for the scientific man, and those who believe most fully in the value of the scientific spirit should be prepared to understand and sympathize with leaders who must obtain general popular approval for their actions.

In practice the adoption of political methods controlled by pure reason could only succeed if they involved a dictatorship and the rule of the majority of the people by a small minority. A realization of this is evident in some of the writings of those scientists who advocate planning.* J. G. Crowther says that "in crises the possession of power is more important than the cultivation of intellectual freedom." † Crowther has evidently forgotten Lord Acton's dictum based on the saying of William Pitt: "Power corrupts, and absolute power corrupts absolutely."

At the present time, therefore, it seems that the many attempts to frame a scientific theory that could guide political action have been wholly unsuccessful. Political action, nevertheless, need not be arbitrary; the long-established fundamental principles remain that have been available to guide human action through the ages. Truth and justice, mercy to the weak, and understanding for the erring are principles that require no formal justification. These are not the

* For a full discussion of planning in relation to science, see J. R. Baker, *Science and the Planned State,* London, George Allen & Unwin, 1945.

† J. G. Crowther, *The Social Relations of Science,* p. 331, New York, The Macmillan Co., 1941.

principles of science; they relate to spiritual rather than natural laws. Nevertheless, the study of the phenomena of society and the reactions of human beings to their social and economic environment, if pursued in accordance with the fundamental principles of science, will lead to a more generalized knowledge of the subject and eventually to methods that can be applied in practice.

If the present system of government cannot change to meet the requirements of the changing world, it must inevitably give way to other systems. That this is so is the claim of many leaders of political thought. But only a few years ago it seemed impossible that industry should ever be organized to use scientific methods. The industries of the last century were, with few exceptions, utterly remote from the methods of thought current in the laboratories of the universities and were controlled largely by "self-made" autocrats. Within our lifetimes all that has changed, and the leaders of our modern industries are often technically trained experts, completely removed from their predecessors as to their outlook and habits of thought. In order to attain a similar result in the field of politics, we need no revolution; we require only an orderly evolution. As Janssen says, "There are very few difficulties that cannot be surmounted by a will strong enough or by study sufficiently profound." *

To effect this orderly change, we must improve the methods of thinking of the public so that they will select suitable governors and then will require from them real leadership and accurate thought. It is both our right and our duty to select for ourselves those who govern us, and the necessary changes can be effected by the proper exercise of that right and duty. The art of government is exceedingly difficult, and it is of the utmost importance, especially in times of transition

---

* In reference to his establishment of an observatory on the summit of Mont Blanc in spite of his lameness. R. A. Gregory, *Discovery or The Spirit and Service of Science,* p. 67, London, Macmillan and Co., Ltd., 1916.

such as the present, that the men chosen as administrators should be selected with the utmost care.

The selection of the best methods of procedure in government, as in science, depends eventually upon judgment, and judgment depends upon the natural capacity of the judge and on his training and experience. In any judgment there will be error, and errors will occur in accordance with the laws of probability. The judgment will be better as the probable error is smaller, but there will always be some error. The administrator, moreover, will suffer from bias. If he is sufficiently objective in mind and sufficiently experienced, he will recognize that and will attempt to make a correction for it just as we correct precision measurements for the "personal equation." We should, therefore, select our methods of government so that there is a maximum chance of arriving at the best judgment, a minimum opportunity for bias, and a probability that the best judgment that can be arrived at will be applied.

In so far as our present methods do not meet these requirements, they should be changed. The most important matter, however, is that we must be prepared to seek out specifically the best men that we have for the functions of government— not always the best in ability but often the best in character, since a man might have first-class judgment and yet be so biased by his ambitions that his decisions would be affected.

In addition to selecting the most suitable leaders, however, the public must be willing to accept their leadership, to value the expression of intelligent thought, and to discount all appeals to emotion and to sectional interests. As Sir Ronald Ross says:

> We must not accept any speculations merely because they now appear pleasant, flattering, or ennobling to us. We must be content to creep upwards step by step, planting each foot on the firmest finding of the moment, using the compass and such other instruments as we have, observing without either despair or contempt the clouds and precipices above and beneath us. Especially our duty at

present is to better our present foothold; to investigate; to comprehend the forces of nature; to set our State rationally in order; to stamp down disease in body, mind, and government; to lighten the monstrous misery of our fellows, not by windy dogmas, but by calm science.*

* R. A. Gregory, *op. cit.,* p. 233.

INDEX

Abbe, Ernst, 217
Abderhalden, E., 130
Académie des Sciences, 85, 86
Academy of Agricultural Science, 183
Accademia del Cimento, 85
Acetic anhydride, 128
Acetylene, 125
Achromatism, 98
Acton, Lord, 233
Adams, Brooks, 72
Agricola, 77
Agriculture, 26
Alaric, 27
Alchemy, 119
Alembert, Jean d', 92
Alexandria, 72, 88, 144
Alexandrian school, 67
Aliphatic chemistry, 125
Alkaloids, 130
Alpha particles, 111
Alpha rays, 136
American Philosophical Society, 86, 87
Amici, Giovanni, 157
Ampère, A. M., 104
Anatomy, 78, 144, 145
Anaximander, 70
Andromeda nebulae, 117
Animal colonies, 178
Animals, respiration of, 152
Anode rays, 108
Anthrax, 166
"Anticipations," 174
Arabic philosophy, 76
Arabic translations, 76
Arabs, settling of, 38

Archaeology and history, 17, 18
Archimedes, 67, 72
Argon, 116, 134
Aristarchus, 72
Aristophanes, 95
Aristotle, 71, 72, 74, 75, 76, 78, 79, 80, 88, 95, 144, 226
Aristotle's elements, 93
Armour Research Foundation, 216
Aromatic chemistry, 125
Arrhenius, Svante, 131, 133
Art, cycles of, 39
  development of, 21
  introduction of, 25
  modern, 39
Aston, F. W., 108, 138, 177
Astrology, 41
Astronomer Royal, 176
Astronomy, 41, 88, 115, 116
Astrophysics, 117
Atlantis, New, 82
Atom, Bohr-Rutherford, 112, 137, 140
  Rutherford, 111, 137
Atomic bombs, 143
Atomic nuclei, 140
  disintegration of, 141, 142, 143
  fission of, 142
Atomic numbers, 137
Atomic structure, 137, 138
Atomic theory, 93, 121
Atomic weights, 138
Attila, 27
Augustine, St., 5, 74
Aurelius, Marcus, 4
Authority, doctrine of, 75